Health Care Ministry

 *Integration Books*

STUDIES IN PASTORAL PSYCHOLOGY,
THEOLOGY, AND SPIRITUALITY
Robert J. Wicks, General Editor

also in this series

Clinical Handbook of Pastoral Counseling
edited by R. Wicks, R. Parsons, and D. Capps
Adolescents in Turmoil, Parents Under Stress
by Richard D. Parsons
Pastoral Marital Therapy
by Stephen Treat and Larry Hof
The Art of Clinical Supervision
edited by B. Estadt, J. Compton and M. Blanchette
The Art of Passingover
by Francis Dorff, O. Praem.
Losses in Later Life
by R. Scott Sullender
Pastoral Care Emergencies
by David K. Switzer
Spirituality and Personal Maturity
by Joann Wolski Conn
Christointegration
by Bernard J. Tyrrell, S.J.
Adult Children of Alcoholics
by Rachel Callahan, C.S.C. and Rea McDonnell, S.S.N.D.

Health Care Ministry
A Handbook for Chaplains

**PREPARED BY THE
NATIONAL ASSOCIATION
OF CATHOLIC CHAPLAINS**

*Helen Hayes, O.S.F.
Cornelius J. van der Poel, C.S.Sp.
editors*

Integration Books

paulist press/new york/mahwah

Library of Congress Cataloging-in-Publication Data

Health care ministry: a handbook for chaplains/prepared by the
  National Association of Catholic Chaplains: Helen Hayes, Cornelius
  J. van der Poel, editors.
      p.   cm.—(Integration books)
  Includes bibliographical references.
  ISBN 0-8091-3136-6
    1. Chaplains, Hospital—Catholic Church—Handbooks, manuals, etc.
  2. Pastoral medicine—Catholic Church—Handbooks, manuals, etc.
  3. Church work with the sick—Handbooks, manuals, etc.   4. Catholic
  Church—Clergy—Handbooks, manuals, etc.   I. Hayes, Helen, 1923–.
  II. Poel, Cornelius J. van der, 1921–   .   III. National
  Association of Catholic Chaplains (U.S.)   IV. Series.
  BX2347.S5H43   1990
  259′.4—dc20   89-48602
                                                                        CIP

Published by Paulist Press
997 Macarthur Boulevard
Mahwah, New Jersey 07430

Printed and bound in the
United States of America

Contents

Contents

III. PASTORAL EDUCATION

TO ALL THE PERSONS WHO SHARE
IN MAKING THE HEALING MISSION OF JESUS
A LIVING REALITY

Robert J. Wicks

Foreword

Ministry to the sick is one of the cornerstones of Christian discipleship, yet until now there has not been a broad-based, contemporary
unified work for Catholics to turn to that would serve as an introduction for them to the themes and considerations of pastoral health
care. This book prepared by the National Association of Catholic
Chaplains under the editorship of Sister Helen Hayes, O.S.F. and
Rev. Cornelius J. van der Poel, C.S.Sp. is an effort to begin filling this
void. Given its scope and fine contributors, it is ideal for full-time
chaplains, parish visitors, pastoral care students and volunteers who
serve in health care settings. In this volume, seminarians, permanent
deacons, priests, vowed religious, and laity who are interested or
involved in this complex and important area have a "handbook" to
turn to for the purpose of introducing them to, or serving as a review
of, the issues and approaches to modern ministry to the sick.

In ministry there are many problems and questions which have
yet to be solved. Nowhere is this more evident than in health care.
Consequently, for those who are seeking solutions, this book will
seem frustrating at times; on the other hand, for those wishing a
greater sensitivity to the challenges and nuances of pastoral health
care, this book will offer much on which to reflect.

Theological issues in pastoral care, ethical decision making, professionalism, pastoral care marketing and administration, quality assurance, ministry in special environments, and pastoral care education are all discussed at length in this book. Although pastoral care
students and full-time chaplains would probably want to read this
book in its entirety, others (e.g. volunteers, parish visitors) would
want to select those topics of most interest to them.

This volume is an edited sourcebook in health care ministry.
Given the varied levels of complexity of the topics and the different
approaches of each of the authors to his or her unique area of focus,
in some cases moving from one area to another, this book will require
readers to shift their vantage point in order to fully appreciate the

material being presented. Given the wealth of experience that each of the contributors brings, and the richness of the material in this book, the effort is well worth it.

This handbook comes at the right time for pastoral health care. Even though there are some fine specialized works being published in the area (i.e. *Health/Medicine and the Faith Traditions Series*), the field has long needed an overview of this type which reflects some of the current thinking of key members of the National Association of Catholic Chaplains. In this sense, the publication of *Health Care Ministry* is an important beginning. Hopefully, it will be the first edition of an ongoing written presence in the field by the NACC.

Helen Hayes, O.S.F.
Cornelius J. van der Poel, C.S.Sp.

Introduction

Perhaps more than most other forms of ministry, health care ministry is essentially interwoven with many different disciplines. In its concern for the spiritual welfare of people, health care ministry is deeply rooted in the theology of the church and in spirituality. Because of the impact of technology on human life, health care ministry has a special interest in medical ethics. Because of its involvement with people whose ordinary life is torn apart through illness, intense and/ or prolonged suffering or death, health care ministry must continuously be in touch with psychology and other behavioral sciences. Since health care ministry is largely practiced in the institutional setting of health care facilities, it needs to incorporate many of the institutional practices, yet it must take care not to become an impersonal reflection of societal bureaucracy. Pastoral ministry must remain deeply personal in its concern for the sick and in giving guidance to health care professionals. There is no doubt that such a confusing complexity demands a special form of professionalism which integrates the deepest human qualities and spirituality with the highest possible degree of familiarity with psychology and medical technology.

It is out of the awareness of this complexity and the numerous questions of chaplains and students of clinical pastoral education that the National Association of Catholic Chaplains has undertaken the composition of this volume. Without trying to give an answer to the innumerable problems that can arise, the National Association of Catholic Chaplains endeavors to present an overview of the pastoral essentials of health care ministry. We want to describe the nature of health care ministry and the way in which spiritual values may be integrated with health care science. This volume tries to explain the nature of the training that is required for this ministry, its incorpora-

3

tion into health care facilities and its subsequent accountability to these facilities as well as to church authorities.

It is impossible to mention all who collaborated in the compilation of this volume, but we want to extend our sincere gratitude to Rev. Edward Dietrich who was one of its initiators but who was unable to stay with it to its completion. We wish to gratefully acknowledge associate editor, Becky Evans, who did an invaluable amount of reading and correcting. Last but far from least, the heart of our gratitude goes out to the many authors who took their time for study, research and reflection, and exchange of ideas. We are also grateful to those who read the manuscripts and gave valuable feedback. They express a deep pastoral concern through searching together for the most effective way to assist their colleagues in the health care ministry.

We are deeply aware that this volume is incomplete. However, despite its shortcomings, we are also confident that it can be of significant help to many people in the health care ministry and to many others who are concerned about the wholeness and well-being of the sick. It is our hope that this effort may carry the Lord's blessing, and that it may support all who so generously give their time and energy for the sake of those in need. It is our prayer that it may be an instrument through which the love of the divine healer strengthens the wounded healers when they reach out to touch and bring comfort to all who are wounded.

I. General Considerations

Robert L. Kinast

Caring for God's Covenant of Freedom: A Theology of Pastoral Care

St. Paul said it most succinctly. "It was for freedom that Christ set us free" (Gal 5:1). The original context for this assertion was Paul's argument with those who insisted on retaining the requirements of the Mosaic law as part of the Christian way of life. In Paul's view this compromised the very meaning of the gospel. "Any of you who seek your justification in the law have severed yourselves from Christ and fallen from God's favor" (Gal 5:4).

The Christian church no longer lives in that tension with the Mosaic law, but it does struggle with a similar tension, one of its own making. The church itself can become a new law, a cluster of customs and prescriptions that take on a life of their own and in effect, even if inadvertently, stifle the Spirit of freedom which Paul proclaimed and Jesus died for.

Freedom is the core which defines the church of Jesus and all its works.[1] As Paul exhorts, "Remember that you have been called to live in freedom" (Gal 5:13). Insofar as the church is a champion of freedom, it is at the service of Jesus' continuing ministry in the world and accomplishes its own purpose.

What is the purpose of the church? It is to care for the covenant which God has initiated with us (and with all of creation) so that both God and we can grow together freely and creatively. It may sound odd, even blasphemous, to suggest that the church helps *God* to grow, much less to grow with us freely and creatively. But such a view takes seriously the terms of the covenant which God has established. There is an unbreakable, interdependent relationship between God and creation, according to which God's freedom to share life with us is conditioned by our own willingness to have God around. We do not have absolute control over God's presence and effectiveness, of course, but we do exercise great influence.

7

Jesus himself experienced this. When the faith of others was strong, as with the centurion (Lk 7:1–10), the Syro-Phoenician woman (Mt 15:21–28), and the paralytic (Lk 5:17–26), it empowered him to free them for a fuller life. When the faith of others was weak, as with the twelve on numerous occasions (e.g. Mt 14:22–33) or his own townspeople (Mk 6:1–6), Jesus was prevented from doing all he could.

Ministry

The church cares best for God's covenant when it liberates people to grow with God in all the dimensions of their lives. This liberating activity of the church is its ministry.[2] The exercise of such ministry may be discussed on three levels.

One level is the *intrapersonal.* This is the irreducible, uniquely individual dimension of each person. Here an unrepeatable combination of influences defines each person as no one else but this person. It is the deepest level of mystery in each human life. At this level a person actively takes in, reworks, and sends out the bits of reality which that person experiences and which shape the actual life of that person.

Gordon Jackson has described this intrapersonal activity in a pastoral care encounter. What does the carer see in the other person?

> Is he or she seeing the other as a center of activity, pulsating with life, ceaselessly forming and reforming himself hundreds of times in the single hour they are together? Is the carer seeing the other as an organism experiencing the world, making the experiencing uniquely his own, and bequeathing what he creates out of those experiences to the next instant of his own becoming and to others? Is the carer envisaging a flow of life in the client so that the clock hour is recording a multitude of changes within him? Is the carer seeing him as a person, a Thou, not static, but a dynamic center of feeling, aiming, imaging, wishing, aspiring, fighting, surrendering activity? And does the carer sense that he or she, too, is a person constantly experiencing the multiplicity of life so that there are never two fractions of time exactly alike?[3]

This dynamic, intrapersonal activity occurs most fully when it occurs most freely. But all sorts of factors can thwart the free exercise of each person's inner life, beginning with the person. When this happens, liberation is called for on the intrapersonal level. However, the individuality of each person is never isolated or self-contained or strictly autonomous. Rather individuality is a pattern of relationships whose center is the person.

This leads to a second level of ministry, the *interpersonal*. The deepest and richest human experiences are those which are shared between persons. Here the complex, mysterious world of each person is creatively fused into a new reality, a more inclusive experience of shared life, what John Patton calls "relational humanness."[4]

Not all interpersonal experiences are freely chosen. Parental and sibling relationships are given, and the traditions of social life encourage friendship with relatives, schoolmates, neighbors, work associates, and other acquaintances. Whether chosen or given, interpersonal relationships constitute a large part of each person's life.

As the potential for enriching human experiences increases at the interpersonal level, so does the potential for enslaving human experiences. The trust and openness of persons to one another carry opportunities for both fulfillment and frustration. Nothing is automatic.

Finally, each person is entwined in a network of people and events and structures which are somewhat removed from the intrapersonal and interpersonal levels, but which greatly influence the actual experience of living. This may be called the *communal-societal* level. Communal refers to primary groupings whereas societal refers to larger, formal organizations.[5]

Often the influence at this level is more pervasive but less easy to identify than the influences at the other levels. For this reason, in the last several years the communal-societal influences have been given more attention, especially in regard to ministry.[6]

Our freedom to enter God's covenant is conditioned by the society in which we live. There are both salvific and demonic elements in our society, and the liberating activity of the church can no more disregard them than Jesus himself could. Even though the gospels portray him as ministering primarily on the intrapersonal and interpersonal levels, Jesus' deep engagement of individuals included the communal-societal circumstances of that time.[7]

To sum up, the church continues Jesus' work by caring for the

covenant which he perfected. It does this most fully when it is engaged in liberative activity. Liberation occurs at intrapersonal, interpersonal, and communal-societal levels. At all of these levels, ministry is for the sake of the interdependent relationship of God and
persons, and persons are understood to be dynamically implicated
with other persons, with nature, and with structures and forces that
cannot always be named or harmonized. In short, all ministry is liberative in a holistic way.

Pastoral Care

Pastoral care is one specific instance of the ministry of the
church. By its very name, as well as its history, pastoral care suggests
the ministry of pastors to the members of a faith community (usually
a parish or congregation). But this is too restrictive. Pastoral care is
exercised not only by pastors and other ordained ministers, but by
every member of the faith community who is in a position to extend
pastoral care. As St. Paul reminded the Galatians, "Help carry one
another's burdens; in that way you will fulfill the law of Christ"
(Gal 6:2).

There is a growing recognition of the fact that everyone is called
to offer pastoral care.[8] Moreover, pastoral care is offered not only in
the context of a local church or to members of a faith community, but
also to people in their work settings, neighborhoods, and other associations.[9]

Such a broadening of the scope of pastoral care is consistent with
the holistic view of ministry described above and with the basic view
of the church as a liberative agent in the world. This is not to say that
the pastoral care of a pastor within a parish or a chaplain within a
hospital does not have special significance. It does, but its significance lies in the fact that it exemplifies in a concentrated and public
way what is happening throughout the shared life of the church in
the world.[10] Pastoral care is not reduced to a pastor's care; it em-
braces all ecclesial care. A pastor's care does not displace ecclesial
care; it gathers it into heightened and explicit experiences.

In addition to its traditional association with the ministry of the
pastor, pastoral care has also frequently been identified with healing.
This has given rise to the sometimes casual substitution of the term
pastoral care for pastoral counseling or pastoral psychotherapy.[11]

The healing involved in pastoral care is both spiritual and psycho-physical. Spiritual healing primarily confronts sin and seeks

sainthood.[12] It focuses on the intrapersonal dimension of life where each person is responsible for that person's decisions and actions. The effects of a person's actions and decisions may indeed be discernible in interpersonal and communal-societal areas, but the core of sin and sanctity is intrapersonal.

Psycho-physical healing is more easily distinguished in the abstract than it is in practice. The advances in psychology and psychotherapy have made it more difficult to say precisely where the psycho-physical leaves off and the spiritual begins in human experiences. This has given rise to some confusion about the precisely pastoral character of healing and care, and therefore some identity confusion about those who offer pastoral care.[13]

Nonetheless, pastoral care responds to the whole person. This includes psycho-physical healing as well as interpersonal and communal-societal levels of life, even if the primary concern of pastoral care is spiritual healing and intrapersonal experience.

Taking all of the foregoing considerations into account, I have developed the following description of pastoral care which I find to be useful.

> Pastoral care is a liberative response to persons in their life cycle development or in moments of crisis by an agent of the church using the resources of the person(s) cared for and the resources of the church in order to facilitate the mutual integration of the person and the community of faith.

A fuller explanation of this description will lead to some specific reflections on pastoral care in a health care environment.

Liberative

If pastoral care is an example of ministry as defined above, then it is liberative. Typically pastoral care focuses on intrapersonal and interpersonal liberation. This is especially true in a health care setting. Illness is a deeply personal experience. It confronts a person with the vulnerability of life and it forces a person to acknowledge the interdependence of life. Interdependence may appear in both the cause of illness (for example, a genetic deficiency, acquired infection, accidents provoked by others) as well as in its cure (health care practice, medical research and technology, supportive concern).

When illness occurs, a person often feels trapped or isolated and usually at the limits of personal resource and self determination. In such circumstances, a liberative response is needed. But liberation does not necessarily mean remedying the illness or removing its effects. It does mean, however, enabling a person to feel in charge of the innermost spirit of self where the covenant with God is nurtured. This level is always a focus of liberative pastoral care regardless of what else can or cannot be done.[14]

All those who contribute to the liberative process in this sense share the ministry of pastoral care. The most obvious examples are those who are designated as pastoral carers (chaplains) and those who work directly with a sick person (medical personnel). Certainly family members and friends are included, but those who administer a health care facility, who maintain it, and who provide support for it also share in the ministry which takes place there.

Often the last group contributes to the communal-societal dimension of liberative ministry, thus complementing the intrapersonal and interpersonal work of the former groups.[15] From this perspective it is not so important that a carer be ordained, be Roman Catholic, or be professionally certified, but that the person's care be liberative.

Responsive

Liberative pastoral care is responsive. This is another way of saying that the person(s) cared for is primary.[16] The needs, capacities, and desires of the person are the chief guide in determining what specific responses are appropriate (liberative) for this person in this situation. Accordingly, listening skills and the ability to form an empathic relationship are more pertinent to pastoral care than other technical or theoretical background.

At the same time, responsiveness does not mean passivity, nor does it mean that a pastoral carer never takes the initiative. Quite the contrary. Responsive pastoral care often raises uncomfortable questions, confronts inconsistent behavior, and challenges escapist attitudes. This is true not only in direct pastoral care of the sick, but in the wider arena of caring for God's covenant in planning, administering, developing, and evaluating a health care facility. The key point is that pastoral care is responsive to the person(s) cared for. Every other stimulus and motivation is secondary.

Persons

A liberative pastoral care response to persons usually occurs in one of two broad areas. One is the life cycle development.[17] This refers to the phases of life which most people in our society ordinarily expect to experience. Anticipating these developments does not mean that a person can always or easily handle them. Marrying well, parenting effectively, aging gracefully, and dying faithfully are primary examples of difficult transitions. Pastoral care is often needed to help a person negotiate changes without clinging fearfully to the past or rushing randomly into the future.

Ordinarily, life cycle developments don't involve health care. But sometimes a person's struggle to manage transitions in life can precipitate health problems such as tension, high blood pressure, and neglected hygiene. On the other hand, some health problems can precipitate a new stage of development—for example, the ability to trust others during an illness, to become more open and intimate about one's feelings, to cultivate a sense of belonging rather than isolation.

Much more frequently, pastoral care deals with the other area of experience—crisis.[18] Some crises can be anticipated, given the makeup and values of our society (for example, crime or divorce); other crises are at least probable (accidents, career changes, relocation, unwanted pregnancies, generational differences). All crises temporarily disrupt a person's usual pattern of behavior and can have paralyzing (unfreeing) effects.

The crises which pastoral care deals with are short-term, recognizable problems. More profound crises require extended counseling and the professional expertise that goes with it. Any illness has a certain crisis quality. Even routine checkups and treatments generate some anxiety and remind a person of the possibility of more serious illness (and eventually, of course, of the terminal event of death). Consequently, pastoral care in a health care setting is responsive to the crisis feeling which a person has, even if the crisis is remote.

The same is true when a crisis confronts health care itself (for example, costs and deficits in providing quality care, hospital policies, ethical questions, unionization). In the latter case, administrators, directors, and the general public may need pastoral care as much as the patients in the health care facilities. Similarly, persons in those positions may be best equipped to extend pastoral care to one another and to model its liberative meaning for other pastoral carers.

Agent

The one who offers pastoral care is an agent of the church. The term "agent of the church" suggests a wider array of ministers than the ordained (pastor), and it also implies that one who exercises pastoral care is acting on behalf of the church. No other designation or delegation is needed to respond in a liberative, caring way to a person in development or in crisis.

This is not to downplay the value of skilled caring. Especially in health care settings, it is important to have some facility for listening attentively and responding empathically. Patients often feel bewildered by the technical environment they find themselves in as well as anxious about the uncertainty of their condition. The untrained instinct of a caring person may be to assure the patient that everything will be all right or to distract the patient from facing feelings honestly. For example, when a promising young athlete was paralyzed in an automobile accident, a well-intentioned carer suggested that he might star in the special olympics someday.

It takes self-discipline and some practice to refrain from telling sick people what they don't need to hear, to concentrate on the signals the patient is sending, to acknowledge one's own anxieties about certain illnesses, to remain present without necessarily solving any problems or eliminating any sickness. And yet this is often the most liberating care that can be given.

At the same time, skilled caring and professionalism need not be stressed in a way that distracts pastoral care from its purpose.[19] The purpose of pastoral care, as of all ministry, is liberation, and the prime resource for liberative pastoral care is the person being cared for.

Inner Resources

The experience of liberation must ultimately come from within. Thus the intrapersonal focus emerges once again. But it must be remembered that a person is never isolated or self-contained. The intrapersonal dimension is always related to interpersonal and communal-societal dimensions. And all three areas are permeated by God's active presence.

External conditions can be established to facilitate freedom, but liberation does not really occur until a person acts on those conditions. To paraphrase St. Paul, Christ has set us free, but we must act on that freedom if we are to share his life. Often persons are not aware of their own inner resources, or they do not feel capable of exercising their power, or they do not want to do so. Any of these attitudes may appear when a person is ill.[20]

In such a situation, the role of the pastoral carer is to help a person recognize inner strengths, to persuade and encourage a person to act on them, to facilitate and support a person's efforts, to do everything short of taking the person's place.

Pastoral care is not limited to the resources of the person cared for. One of the key additional resources is the interpersonal relationship established between the carer and the one cared for. Through this relationship many other resources can be effectively channeled to the person, especially the resources of the faith community.

Church Resources

Pastoral care has traditionally derived its distinctiveness from the use of explicit, religious resources like scripture, sacraments, formal or spontaneous prayer, devotions, and religious symbols (such as the crucifix, relics, or rosary beads). Sometimes a pastoral carer can become compulsive about using these resources, with the result that they become the most important aspect of a pastoral care encounter and the carer neglects to engage the person being cared for. In that case liberative ministry is unlikely to occur.

The other extreme, of course, is the pastoral carer who never uses the explicit resources of the church, relying instead on helping and counseling techniques borrowed from other professions. Liberative ministry occurs in the balance.[21]

The key to discerning the balance is the person being cared for. From this vantage point (rather than the carer's preferences or assumptions or habits), decisions are made about the use of the resources of the church, including the celebration of the sacraments.

Sacraments

The sacraments have played a major role in the Roman Catholic tradition of pastoral care.[22] These specific, ritual sacraments are concentrated experiences of a more pervasive sacramentality wherein God meets us in the ordinary circumstances of our lives and uses these very circumstances to share life with us more fully.[23]

The seven sacraments of the Roman Catholic Church have a

special role to play in the sacramentality of life, because they help us
focus our attention and energy on the permeating presence and liberating action of God in our midst. The sacraments which occur most
frequently in pastoral care ministry (anointing, eucharist-viaticum,
reconciliation) have a similar effect on our experience of pastoral
care and its liberative quality.

This point is made clear in the revised rite of anointing and
viaticum which the rite situates in the general pastoral care of the
sick.[24] As the introduction to the first part of the rite says:

> The concern that Christ showed for the bodily and spiritual
> welfare of those who are ill is continued by the church in its
> ministry to the sick. This ministry is the common responsi-
> bility of all Christians, who should visit the sick, remember
> them in prayer, and celebrate the sacraments with them.
> The family and friends of the sick, doctors and others who
> care for them, and priests with pastoral responsibilities have
> a particular share in this ministry of comfort. Through words
> of encouragement and faith they can help the sick to unite
> themselves with the sufferings of Christ for the good of
> God's people (#43).

In this statement it is clear that the church's pastoral care ministry is a continuation of Jesus' ministry. In addition, all share in this
work, and the ultimate aim is to assist the person to see the present
illness in relation to that person's experience of God and membership
in the church.

This is, in effect, liberating a person inwardly to allow God to be
experienced in the midst of the illness. When this occurs, it becomes
a sign to others which enables them to experience God more deeply
in their lives. As the rite says:

> The role of the sick in the church is to be a reminder to
> others of the essential or higher things. By their witness the
> sick show that our mortal life must be redeemed through the
> mystery of Christ's death and resurrection (#3).
> The sick person is not the only one who should fight against
> illness. Doctors and all who are devoted in any way to caring
> for the sick should consider it their duty to use all the means
> which in their judgment may help the sick, both physically
> and spiritually. In so doing, they are fulfilling the command
> of Christ to visit the sick, for Christ implied that those who

visit the sick should be concerned for the whole person and offer both physical relief and spiritual comfort (#4).

This holistic view is given sacramental concentration through the rites of anointing and viaticum (with reconciliation if needed). These specific sacraments respond to the person's need to be liberated from the threat to faith which serious illness can pose and from fear at the final transition from this life to the next.

Those who are seriously ill need the special help of God's grace in this time of anxiety, lest they be broken in spirit and, under the pressure of temptation, perhaps weakened in their faith (#5).

Unlike pastoral care in general, these sacramental expressions are ordinarily reserved to the ordained (and superiors of clerical religious institutes—#16, #29). This can pose a problem pastorally, if not theologically. When the agent of the church who has been ministering to a seriously ill person is not ordained and therefore cannot reconcile the person sacramentally, or anoint the person, or ordinarily bring viaticum (#29), the integrity and wholeness of the ministry is interrupted. The liberative pastoral care which has brought the person to the very point of seeking anointing, reconciliation, or viaticum is turned over to another person, who possesses the requisite ordination.

The pastoral practice of caring for the sick sacramentally continues to evolve. Hopefully, it will resolve the current tensions so that the primary concern is the persons cared for rather than a custom of the church or a theology which overlooks the actual experience of pastoral care in the church today.

Despite these difficulties, the revised rite clearly situates the celebration of the sacraments in the context of the total pastoral care of a person. The same configuration can be applied to other resources of the church like scripture, prayer, and religious objects. When this is done appropriately, that is, for the sake of the person, taking account of the actual conditions, the church as a whole benefits.

Mutual Integration

The church as a whole benefits because its shared experience of spirit life is deepened, intensified, and advanced by every instance of liberative pastoral care. This may not appear visibly, especially if the pastoral care occurs between two persons in a relatively private and brief encounter. But the church *is* its shared life with God; it *is* its covenant experience. Each time the covenant is renewed in one person's life, each time the freedom of Jesus is actualized in one person's situation, the whole church shares that experience.

Obviously, there are special benefits when people share consciously in the experience of another person's growth in freedom. This is why the rite of the pastoral care of the sick (to take just one sacramental example) encourages the presence of members of the faith community for pastoral care, anointing, and viaticum.

> It is thus especially fitting that all baptized Christians share in this ministry of mutual charity within the body of Christ by doing all that they can to help the sick return to health, by showing love for the sick, and by celebrating the sacraments with them. Like the other sacraments, these too have a community aspect, which should be brought out as much as possible when they are celebrated (#33).

When members of a faith community are present, the interpersonal and communal dimensions of pastoral care are enhanced. The effect may consist of a new awareness of how important we are to one another, or a new appreciation of how we actually enter each other's experience, or a new recognition of one person's ability to contribute to another who is in need. Whenever a member of the community is liberated through pastoral care ministry, the whole community is affected by at least that one additional experience. To this degree, pastoral care also liberates the community from its familiar routines and assumptions and patterns.

Thus, pastoral care reaffirms the holistic character of all ministry, which gathers up the intrapersonal, interpersonal, and communal-societal dimensions of life and opens them to further experience and expansion. What is received from a pastoral care encounter is poured back out, through the members of the church, into the world at large. This is the overall vision of pastoral care and the ultimate theological statement about it. Summarizing this vision in regard to Jesus' indwelling of the church, Gerald Janzen has said:

> His spiritual indwelling may be understood in terms of what St. Paul calls the freedom for which Christ has set us free (Gal 5:1 and the whole context with its emphasis on freedom and Spirit). Jesus envisages us, his followers, so intensely in

terms of our own potential, intrinsic worth and absolute selfhood that when this gift of freedom is mediated through his body the church, it may be experienced as having the capacity to set us free from the coercive and overwhelming momentum of our own past and of the world as settled. We are set free to become children of God, free to inherit the selfhood that God endows by his own envisagement of us as in his own image. In this way of understanding it, the church does in fact act as the mediator of the Spirit of Christ.[25]

In the same way the church cares for the covenant of God and through its care continues the ministry of Jesus. In pastoral care and in all its ministries, the church is to be guided by the fundamental conviction that it was for freedom that Christ set us free.

Notes

1. For recent discussions of Christian freedom, see Schubert Ogden, *Faith and Freedom* (Nashville: Abingdon Press) 1979; Delwin Brown, *To Set at Liberty* (Maryknoll: Orbis Books) 1981.

2. Howard Clinebell has described this as a holistic liberation-growth model of ministry. See his *Basic Types of Pastoral Care and Counseling* (Nashville: Abingdon Press, 1984) pp. 25–47.

3. Gordon E. Jackson, *Pastoral Care and Process Theology* (Lanham: The University Press of America, 1981) pp. 1–2.

4. John Patton, *Pastoral Counseling: A Ministry of the Church* (Nashville: Abingdon Press, 1983) pp. 19–37.

5. See, for example, the treatment in Evelyn Eaton Whitehead and James D. Whitehead, *Community of Faith* (New York: The Seabury Press, 1982) pp. 19–34.

6. See, for example, Don S. Browning, *Religious Ethics and Pastoral Care* (Philadelphia: Fortress Press) 1983; James N. Poling and Donald E. Miller, *Foundations for a Practical Theology of Ministry* (Nashville: Abingdon Press) 1985.

7. For an application of this point, see Robert L. Kinast, "Parish Social Ministry: Challenges and Limits," *Church*, 1 (Summer 1985) pp. 30–35.

8. See, for example, Diane Detwiler-Zapp and William Caveness Dixon, *Lay Caregiving* (Philadelphia: Fortress Press) 1982; Howard W. Stone, *The Caring Church* (San Francisco: Harper and Row) 1983; Kenneth C. Haug, *Christian Caregiving* (Minneapolis: Augsburg) 1984.

9. See Parker Rossmann and Gaylord Noyce, *Helping People Care on the Job* (Valley Forge: Judson Press) 1985; Robert L. Kinast, *Caring for Society: A Theological Interpretation of Lay Ministry* (Chicago: The Thomas More Press) 1985.

10. In one sense this parallels the relationship between the sacraments and the sacramentality of the church. The sacraments are specific, ritualized moments which presuppose and express a more pervasive, spontaneous experience of grace.

11. For the distinction among these terms, see Howard Clinebell, *Basic Types*, p. 26.

12. See Edward E. Thornton, "Finding Center in Pastoral Care," in *Spiritual Dimensions of Pastoral Care*, Gerald L. Borchert and Andrew D. Lester, eds. (Philadelphia: The Westminster Press, 1985) pp. 11–27.

13. See William V. Arnold, *Introduction to Pastoral Care* (Philadelphia: The Westminster Press, 1982) pp. 15–153.

14. See, for example, Donald Capps, *Pastoral Care: A Thematic Approach* (Philadelphia: The Westminster Press) 1979; John B. Cobb, Jr., *Theology and Pastoral Care* (Philadelphia: The Fortress Press) 1977.

15. See the collection of readings entitled *The Ministry of Healing* (St. Louis: The Catholic Health Association of the U.S., 1981) pp. 70–121.

16. See C. W. Brister, *Pastoral Care in the Church* (San Francisco: Harper and Row, 1977) pp. 34–56.

17. See Donald Capps, *Life Cycle Theory and Pastoral Care* (Philadelphia: The Fortress Press) 1983.

18. See Charles V. Gerkin, *Crisis Experience in Modern Life: Theory and Theology for Pastoral Care* (Nashville: Abingdon Press) 1979.

19. See Alastair Campbell, *Professionalism and Pastoral Care* (Philadelphia: The Fortress Press) 1985.

20. One of the significant recent developments in health care is the holistic health movement, which puts great emphasis on the patient's powers to heal and foster wellness.

21. See Paul Pruyser, *The Minister as Diagnostician* (Philadelphia: The Westminster Press) 1976; Thomas C. Oden, *Care of Souls in the Classic Tradition* (Philadelphia: Fortress Press) 1984.

22. For the implications of the restored catechumenate for pastoral care, see Regis Duffy, *A Roman Catholic Theology of Pastoral Care* (Philadelphia: Fortress Press) 1983. For a discussion of sacra-

ments and pastoral care, see Robert L. Kinast, *Sacramental Pastoral Care* (New York: Pueblo Publishing Co.) 1988.

23. See Bernard Cook, *Sacraments and Sacramentality* (Mystic: The Twenty-Third Press) 1983.

24. See *The Rites of the Catholic Church as Revised by the Second Vatican Council* (New York: Pueblo Publishing Co., 1983) pp. 593–743. References are taken from this edition and are cited in the text by paragraph numbers.

25. J. Gerald Janzen, "Modes of Presence and the Communion of Saints," *Religious Experience and Process Theology*, Harry James Cargas and Bernard Lee, eds. (New York: Paulist Press, 1976) p. 168.

Corrine Bayley, C.S.J.

The Chaplain and Ethical Decision Making

A person who wants to be confronted with a minimum of ethical choices during the working day should not choose a career in health care. It would be hard to think of a profession more visited with troubling decisions than one that comes into daily contact with people who are ill, children who are dying, families who are confused, angry or grieving, and staff who are torn between conflicting loyalties. The possibilities for healing and transformation in such a setting are great, of course, but they do not come without a price.

Chaplains are often called on to help people who are struggling with an ethical dilemma. To function effectively in this role, a chaplain should have some understanding of ethics and ethical decision making. This chapter will offer some beginning suggestions in each of these topics and conclude with a brief discussion of hospital ethics committees and the chaplain's contribution as a member.

First, a sort of warning. Unfortunately, people often expect chaplains to know "the right thing to do." This expectation arises from some vague belief that those who have chosen religion as a profession are somehow gifted with divine inspiration. They are thought to have special access to the mind of God, and therefore to clarity in the midst of confusion. Others—not as eager to ascribe divine powers to chaplains—assume that they have spent years studying ethics and morality, and hence either know the answers or know where to find them.

Accepting the role of moral seer and spokesperson for the divine may be tempting; in fact, those who have fallen into this trap have made life more difficult for their colleagues who try to avoid it. However, mature ethical decision making requires far more than infused knowledge or authoritative pronouncements. Convincing others of this, while at the same time modeling for them an alternative method of moral deliberation, is something chaplains need to do. Chaplains must be clear about their role and the extent of their expertise in ethics. If they are not, others will fill the vacuum with unrealistic expectations and unspoken assumptions that vary from person to person and that are often at odds with the chaplain's own self-perceptions.

It is important to have a basic understanding of the nature of ethics. Ethics has been used to refer to everything from etiquette to custom, to rules and regulations, to religious beliefs, to moral behavior, to philosophical study. A succinct definition of ethics is "the art-science which seeks to bring sensitivity and method to the discernment of moral values."[1]

Ethics is an art because it involves creativity, imagination, affectivity and intuition. It requires its students (and we are all lifelong students of ethics) to taste deeply of life, to reflect on its mysteries, to shape it in various ways, and to share it with others. There is something ultimately inexplicable in art; so too in ethics. As Pascal put it, "We know truth not only by the reason, but also by the heart. . . . The heart has its reasons which reason does not know."[2]

Ethics is a science because it uses methods, systems, analyses of data, comparisons, rationality and inquiry. It is not the kind of science (if indeed there is any) that is perfectly precise, objective and absolute. It is, however, the kind of science that offers more than mere speculation and subjectivity.

Ethics involves discernment, a term with which most chaplains are familiar. In the Christian tradition, discernment involves openness, serious reflection, weighing of pros and cons, and dialogue with others.

Ethics is a branch of philosophy which deals with the principles governing right conduct. It asks and attempts to answer such questions as: Who is right? What is good? What is my duty or obligation? What is the best thing to do in this situation? How should I decide? The aim of ethics is to discover, formulate and defend fundamental principles regarding morally right action. Ethics attempts to arrive at reasonable resolutions of issues through the use of logical argumentation, careful consideration of relevant information, reliance on principles which are consistent and universal, and weighing of alternative courses of action.

One does not have to be a philosopher to "do ethics." In fact, we are all engaged in the ethical life every day in many of the choices we make. Ethics is concerned with values, with moral principles, and with how people ought to behave toward each other. A person trying to make a good ethical judgment seeks to promote good and minimize harm. Such a person tries to do the just thing, the honest thing, the faithful thing, the right thing. How does one know which acts fall into these categories? Sometimes it is very clear, but sometimes it is not at all clear. What should you do if you have promised you would keep a confidence, and now it turns out that keeping it will harm someone else? What should a doctor do if the parents of a newborn child direct that the infant not be treated? What should a nurse do if a patient keeps asking for information and the physician refuses to give it? In all of these cases, the person is faced with an ethical dilemma. A dilemma by definition is a situation involving a choice between unsatisfactory alternatives. Every choice contains both some good and some harm. In a dilemma there are conflicts among duties, loyalties, rights, values, or principles.

It is important to remember that an ethical dilemma is a conflict between ethical goods—for example, between the patient's right to refuse treatment and the principle of beneficence (doing good for the patient). If the conflict does not involve ethical principles, it is not an ethical dilemma. It may be a communication problem, an administrative or legal uncertainty, or a garden variety personality conflict. For it to be an ethical dilemma, it must involve a choice and it must involve ethical harms and benefits. An ethical dilemma is often articulated in question form beginning with "should"—e.g., Should this seriously handicapped newborn be aggressively treated?

An individual or group faced with an ethical dilemma will have complex issues to sort out. What is needed is a process or method for structuring, clarifying and resolving the issues. Sometimes this is called an ethical workup or a model for ethical decision making. What follows is a suggestion for such a process. It involves five major steps:

1. Identify the ethical dilemma.

2. Gather all the pertinent facts.

3. Identify the ethical principle(s) in conflict and choose the one(s) that should have priority.

4. Identify alternative courses of action and the consequences of each.

5. Make a decision (or recommendation) and consider how it should be carried out.

Identify the Ethical Dilemma

Step 1 is to identify the ethical dilemma. If it is a personal dilemma about what he/she should do in a situation, the chaplain will be able to identify it fairly easily. For example, my dilemma is: Should I share information I received in confidence in order that harm to another person will be avoided?

Identifying a dilemma experienced by another person may take more probing, particularly since most people are not skilled at stating dilemmas in their simplest terms. Often the concern is expressed in an incoherent way or in the form of a narrative that stops short of naming the dilemma. For example, a nurse may tell the chaplain that a patient on dialysis has been talking about stopping treatment, the family is ambiguous, the physician evasive, and one staff member is concerned about suicide. There are several potential ethical dilemmas lurking in that scenario, but none is as yet clearly evident. It may be that none has emerged yet, but the nurse anticipates that one will. Or it may be that she needs help in formulating the dilemma that she feels she is facing. Often the dilemma cannot be clearly identified until further facts are obtained, so step 1 is not always completed first.

Gather All Pertinent Facts

Step 2 is to gather all the pertinent facts. If the dilemma is already clear, at this stage more data will be collected to help resolve it. If it is not clear, it will either become so or the facts will demonstrate that there is no dilemma after all. It is often discovered in the fact-gathering process that communication has been lacking somewhere along the line and what was perceived as an ethical dilemma is a problem of another sort.

The nature of the dilemma will dictate what facts need to be assessed. For dilemmas involving patient care, the following five categories should be explored: the patient's medical condition, the patient's wishes, the views of the care-givers, the views of family and friends, and legal, administrative or other external factors.

In the example of the dialysis patient above, medical facts can be discovered through such questions as: What is the patient's current medical status? Are there other contributing medical conditions? What is the patient's prognosis? Has a second opinion been obtained? What treatments are possible? What is the probable life-expectancy of the patient, and general condition if dialysis is continued? What are the risks and the side-effects of continued treatment? Is the patient a candidate for a kidney transplant? Since many of the ethical decisions to be made turn on the diagnosis and prognosis of a patient, the importance of gathering accurate and comprehensive medical data cannot be emphasized too strongly.

If the patient is competent, the patient's wishes are a critical factor in decision making. The extent of the patient's knowledge and understanding of his or her condition should be thoroughly assessed. In the example of the dialysis patient, it is important to know exactly what the patient's concerns and convictions are and on what they are based. If the patient is saying that he or she wants to stop dialysis, it is important to know why. Are the reasons based on something that could change, e.g. temporary depression or inadequate medication? Are the patient's wishes consistent or do they fluctuate from time to time? To whom has the patient expressed his or her views? Is there any reason to challenge that person's interpretation? Getting clear about the patient's preference involves making sure that the patient has thorough and adequate information upon which to base a personal decision.

If the patient is not competent, one question that needs to be asked is whether he or she is ever expected to regain competence. Other questions include: Did the patient ever make a clear statement that would indicate what the patient's wishes would be in circumstances such as these? Has the patient prepared a written statement regarding his or her wishes? If the patient has made no clear statement, is there information from anyone regarding what the patient might have wanted or might reasonably be assumed to have wanted in such circumstances?

What are the views of the patient's primary care-givers—physicians, nurses, social workers, respiratory therapists, etc.? Often these individuals have information about the patient and/or family that would be helpful in decision making. In addition, it is important to know if they are experiencing any personal conflicts, either about their role or about possible decisions that might be made. If there are disagreements among the health care team, they need to be identified and explored.

The views of family and friends of the patient are important, particularly if the patient is not able to speak for himself or herself. One of the difficulties is in identifying who should be considered family. Beyond immediate family (parents, children, spouses, siblings), are grandparents, aunts, uncles, cousins, etc. considered family? And what about the role of non-family friends? In sorting this out, it is important to remember why we are interested in the views of others in the first place. Beyond an ill-defined legal reason, we are mainly interested in finding out what the patient would have wanted or in discovering someone who will act in the patient's best interest. This person may or may not be a family member. A recent court case in California states that in seeking to identify appropriate surrogates (representatives) of the patient with whom the health care provider should consult regarding treatment issues, one should consider immediate family members or non-family friends who: "a) are in the best position to know the patient's feelings and desires regarding treatment, b) would be most affected by the treatment decision, c) are concerned for the patient's comfort and welfare, and d) have expressed an interest in the patient by visits or inquiries to the patient's physician or hospital staff."[3]

Like the patient, the family and/or friends should be given adequate information on which to base their decisions or recommendations. If family members disagree about what should be done and the patient is incompetent, a great deal of work may need to be done with family members to effect a reconciliation of views. Many physicians are reluctant to take even those actions they deem appropriate on the patient's behalf in the face of disagreement among family.

Finally, legal, administrative, and other external factors should be considered. For example, are there state statutes or case laws that apply to this situation? What potential liability might be present? Are there hospital policies and/or guidelines that apply? Are there others (inside or outside the institution) who should be given information and/or asked for an opinion? Would it help to consult the literature for any aspect of this case? Is expense to this patient and/or to society a factor in this case? What should the weight of this consideration be?

The importance of having accurate facts cannot be overestimated. The more complex the situation and the more actors there are in the drama, the more potential there is for misrepresentation of facts. This unfortunately occurs far too often in hospital settings and leads both to a misrepresentation of the problem and to inappropriate responses to it.

Identify, Prioritize Ethical Principles in Conflict

The third step is to identify the ethical principles in conflict and choose the ones that should have priority. By the time the facts have been gathered, the ethical dilemma will be identified if it has not been previously. It will be recalled that an ethical dilemma involves a conflict among ethical principles. It could turn out that, in the example given above, the ethical dilemma is identified as: "Should we support this patient's choice to discontinue renal dialysis?" If the staff feels that the patient is doing well on dialysis and could benefit further from it, the ethical principles in conflict are autonomy, or the patient's right to refuse treatment, and beneficence, or "doing good" for the patient. The ethical principles most frequently involved in clinical situations are patient autonomy, beneficence, non-maleficence and justice.

Patient autonomy has received a lot of attention in the bioethics literature recently. It is generally believed that respect for persons requires us to allow the patient to choose whether he or she wants to be treated. Indeed, our legal doctrine of informed consent is based on that premise. There are some rare exceptions to the presumption of following the patient's wishes, as in the clear case of the patient wanting the hospital to assist with suicide, or in the case of the patient demanding medically inappropriate or unreasonable treatment. However, the preferences of patients ordinarily take priority over other considerations. A necessary condition for true patient autonomy is that the patient has received full and accurate information about his or her condition, including risks and benefits of treatment as well as alternative treatments.

A caveat needs to be offered in connection with the principle of autonomy. For years, patients were treated in a paternalistic way in which decisions were often made for them without their knowledge or genuine consent. This was clearly inappropriate and needed to be righted. However, the current emphasis on autonomy threatens in some cases to be as unkind and disrespectful of the patient as was paternalism. The principle of autonomy is not well served if health professionals merely supply information to the patient and leave him or her to decide in isolation. It must be remembered that a sick person is not merely a well person with a disease. Sickness affects us not only physically, but also socially, emotionally, and cognitively. It can be extraordinarily difficult to make clear decisions about one's body, indeed one's life, when one is seriously ill. Sensitivity to this on the part of the care-givers will enhance respect for persons, on which autonomy is based.

A second important principle is beneficence, or doing good for others. In considering medical interventions, treatment that will reverse illness, restore health, provide comfort, or relieve suffering is regarded as beneficial.

The Catholic Church has been a leader in clarifying the underlying principles to be considered in choices about foregoing treatment. In the "Declaration on Euthanasia" of June 1980, the Vatican Congregation for the Doctrine of the Faith summarized a long tradition in the following words:

> It is also permissible to make do with the normal means that medicine can offer. Therefore, one cannot impose on anyone the obligation to have recourse to a technique which is already in use, but which carries a risk or is burdensome. Such a refusal is not the equivalent of suicide; on the contrary, it should be considered as an acceptance of the human condition or a wish to avoid the application of a medical procedure disproportionate to the results that can be expected, or a desire not to impose excessive expense on the family or the community.[4]

A decision about forgoing treatment, then, involves a balancing of the burdens of treatment and the benefits of treatment. A patient's best interests are rarely served by imposing a burden without corresponding benefit.

A third principle critical in many ethical dilemmas is non-maleficence. In fact, this is often spoken of as the "first principle," holding as it does that persons should never be directly harmed. One of the issues increasingly discussed today is whether it is harmful (or, conversely, could be considered beneficial) to withdraw artificial nutrition and hydration from a patient. The principles of beneficence and non-maleficence, combined with accurate medical facts, should be helpful guides in sorting out this question on a case-by-case basis.

The principle of justice holds that people in similar situations should be treated similarly. Persons should be treated fairly and should not be discriminated against on the basis of factors that may make them vulnerable, such as mental ability, social contribution or financial status. In situations involving handicapped newborns, the principle of justice is often at stake. Access to care by the medically poor is also a justice issue of growing proportions.

Setting priorities among the ethical principles is always difficult for two reasons: first, because it is hard to choose between goods, and, second, because it is never as clear as one would like what the consequences of one's choice will be. Establishing the primary ethical principles, however, is the prelude to the final decision. In establishing priorities among principles, careful attention should be paid to the reasons for one's choice. Reasons should take into consideration both short and long range consequences.

People may still disagree about which principles are most important, and they should be asked to identify the underlying norms that support their view. It is often true that a defensible case could be made for giving priority to different principles. The case can be made much more persuasively if reasons are articulated and the issues carefully considered. That is, of course, what the process is all about. The alternative is a decision method that more resembles a political debate, replete with rhetoric, unsubstantiated claims, power plays and manipulation of facts. Following a careful process does not remove discomfort or disagreement, but at least people will know what they disagree about. They will understand each other's language and the reasons for different conclusions.

Identify Alternative Courses of Action and Their Consequences

The fourth step in the process is to consider alternative courses of action. Like the other steps, this is not a discrete one, but overlaps with them. As principles are identified, courses of action will be suggested. Brainstorming and consideration of several alternatives should be a part of this step. In the process, everyone will have a chance to think through and make arguments for and against various alternatives. This broadens thinking and can help avoid polarization. Often ideas are suggested that can help with the implementation of the final decision.

The possible short and long range consequences of alternatives should be identified also. What is likely to happen to the various people involved if such and such is done? Who may be harmed in the short or long run? Who will be benefited in the short or long run? Concern for the individual patient as well as the consequences for other patients and for society should be considered.

Make a Decision

The fifth and final step is to make a decision. The burden of this, of course, falls on the person(s) who are responsible. Others can assist by going through the first four steps with them: identifying the facts, the principles, and a range of reasonable ethical options. But, finally, someone has to make a difficult choice.

Ethical dilemmas never arise when we are ready for them and they always require more reflection time than we have. The above process can be shortened to less than an hour, or it may take place over several days. However, it cannot take away the tension, doubt and anxiety experienced in the face of a true dilemma. Choosing one value at the expense of another causes psychic pain, regardless of how careful the analysis has been. Unfortunately, there are no absolute or definitive answers in ethics.

In the past few years, many hospitals have formed ethics committees in response to increasingly complex ethical issues. These committees are usually multidisciplinary and deal with a wide range of bioethical issues—for example, concerns about the use of life-prolonging technology in both adults and newborns, allocating resources, dealing with inter-professional conflicts over ethical issues, deciding about the use of reproductive technologies, and making sure the legitimate rights of all in the institution are respected.

The ethics committee serves three primary functions: education, the development of policies and/or guidelines, and consultation. It is likely that none of the committee members will be "experts" in bioethics[5] and they will therefore learn together. Education of committee members themselves should be one of the first items on the agenda of a newly formed committee.

Ethics committees are advisory bodies. They can provide a great service in developing and referring for approval guidelines on such topics as Do Not Resuscitate orders and the treatment of seriously ill newborns. They can, as they develop some expertise, be a very valuable resource for those in the hospital who are faced with an ethical dilemma and would like some help thinking it through.

Each hospital will develop its own guidelines for the formation and function of ethics committees and will find assistance from an increasing number of books and articles on the subject.[6]

Chaplains can be especially valuable members of ethics committees because they have an insight into the feelings and concerns of patients and families, and are often present when ethical decisions are made. Patients and families often need help in sorting out their values and beliefs, though they may not recognize the need in those terms. It would seem that at no time is the need to clarify one's values more urgent than in deciding on measures that will affect the quality and perhaps the continuation of one's life. Yet at the very time such deliberation is most needed, it is frequently the most difficult. The values and beliefs in question are often the most deeply embedded, as well as perhaps the least defined and developed. The concerns are spiritual. Do I really believe in God? Have I led a good life? How can I better prepare for death? What does my church say about limiting treatment? All of these are questions that a chaplain can help a patient think through, not as decision maker, but as companion and facilitator.

Chaplains are often very good listeners, a skill greatly needed by ethics committee members. Being able to appreciate others' points of view as well as being able to articulate one's own is necessary for a contributing ethics committee member. Another quality much in demand is that of being a critical thinker. By that is meant someone who can work through the process described above, ask probing questions, and challenge conventional wisdom. A chaplain is a "lay person" as opposed to a health professional, and hence is in a good position to revisit issues that carry the unspoken label "we've always done it that way." Chaplains also affirm values that most people have intuitively: honesty, respect for persons, gentleness with people who are suffering—and that includes doctors and nurses; they too need people to minister to them. Chaplains bring a pastoral perspective that is important at all levels of the institution.

Chaplains also perform a unique function in that they can be counted on to take religious beliefs very seriously. Whether the patient is a Jehovah's Witness, a Christian Scientist, a Seventh Day Adventist or a Catholic, his or her choices may be strongly influenced by religious beliefs. Health professionals need to be reminded that these are important and should be weighed seriously. The chaplain is often an advocate for the patient in this regard.

While disappointing the expectations of some that they will provide answers, chaplains perform a far more valuable service by focusing on underlying principles and inviting all to consider what our traditional values might say to complex new situations. Particularly in Catholic hospitals, one expects basic theological beliefs to form the foundation for ethical decision making. Chaplains perform perhaps their most valuable service not only by reminding others of these beliefs, but by manifesting a deep personal commitment to them.

There are several ways to state the theological beliefs which form a basis for Christian ethics. The following are offered as a conclusion to this chapter and as an impetus for further reflection:

1. Persons are created by a loving God, and are therefore inherently good and worthy of respect.

2. Like God, people are relational, and therefore need the support of others in community.

3. Jesus gave new meaning to suffering and death, a meaning which transforms those realities in our own lives.

4. We have been redeemed by Jesus, but are still sinful and limited, and therefore in need of reconciliation.

5. Jesus was a healer of persons who attended to their spirit as well as to their body.

6. God has a preferential love for the poor, weak and vulnerable, and therefore we have a special responsibility toward them.

7. Jesus was incarnate and lived among us as a human being. Therefore we know the Lord through our contacts with each other.

The role of the chaplain in ethical decision making has many dimensions. A cursory knowledge of ethics and the process of decision making, a realistic perception of one's own role, and a commitment to basic theological beliefs will enhance the quality of the chaplain's contributions.

Notes

1. Daniel C. Maguire, *The Moral Choice* (Garden City: Doubleday, 1978) p. 110.

2. Blaise Pascal, *Pensées* (New York: Washington Square Press, 1965) Nos. 282 and 277.

3. Barber v. Superior Court 147 Cal. App. 3d 1006, 1021, fn. 2 (1983).

4. In Donald McCarthy and Albert Moraczewski, *Moral Responsibility in Prolonging Life Decisions* (St. Louis: Pope John Center, 1981) p. 295.

5. The term "bioethics" was coined in the early 1970s to refer in a shorthand way to the many new ethical issues that are arising for individuals as well as for society at large as a result of developments in medicine and the life sciences. Some prefer the term "biomedical ethics" or "medical ethics." This latter term is felt by many to be too narrow, because for years it has referred primarily to the ethics of physicians.

6. In addition to those in the resource list, the following books provide some helpful information:

> Cranford, R. E. and Doudera, A. E., ed. *Institutional Ethics Committees and Health Care Decision Making.* Ann Arbor: Health Administration Press, 1984.

34 *Health Care Ministry*

Hosford, B. *Bioethics Committees: The Health Care Provider's Guide.* Rockville: Aspen Systems Corporation, 1986.
Kelly, M. J. and McCarthy, D. G., ed. *Ethics Committees: A Challenge for Catholic Health Care.* St. Louis: Catholic Health Association of the United States and Pope John Center, 1984.

Bioethics Resources

General Texts

Beauchamp, T., and Childress, J. *Principles of Biomedical Ethics.* New York: Oxford University Press, 1979. *A clear, concise textbook explaining basic ethical principles and showing how they are applied to major issues in bioethics such as informed consent, risk/benefit assessment, confidentiality, and decisions to terminate therapy. Cases and codes of ethics are included.*
Beauchamp, T., and Walters, L. *Contemporary Issues in Bioethics,* Second Edition. Belmont: Wadsworth Publishing Co., 1982. *An anthology of important essays dealing with such topics as ethical theory, concepts of health and disease, patients' rights and professional responsibilities, abortion, euthanasia, allocation of medical resources, research.*
McCormick, R. *Health and Medicine in the Catholic Tradition.* New York: Crossroad, 1984. *This book deals with major questions relating to sexual, medical and familial morality from the Roman Catholic point of view. Among the issues discussed are birth control and responsible parenthood, abortion, treatment of newborns with disabilities, life-prolonging treatment of the dying, ethical guidelines for care of the retarded and aged, and justice in health care.*
O'Rourke, K., and Ashley, B. *Health Care Ethics: A Theological Analysis.* St. Louis: The Catholic Health Association, 1982. *This book explains the traditional Catholic teaching on such things as personhood, the right to health, bioethical decision making, abortion, human experimentation, reproductive technologies, genetic engineering, suffering, and death.*

Special Issues

Jameton, A. *Nursing Practice: The Ethical Issues.* Englewood Cliffs: Prentice-Hall, Inc., 1984. *Though intended for nurses, this well written and researched text is helpful to chaplains as they seek to*

understand the ethical issues faced by nurses and all non-physicians. It includes a balanced mixture of theory and practice.
President's Commission for the Study of Ethical Problems in Medicine and Biomedical and Behavioral Research. *Deciding To Forego Life-Sustaining Treatment.* Washington, DC: U.S. Government Printing Office, 1983. *This is an excellent summary of the philosophical principles and practical problems involved in decisions to forego treatment.*
Ross, J. W., Bayley, C., Michel, V., and Pugh, D. *The Ethics Committee Manual.* To be published by the American Hospital Association. *This book is a practical reference for those serving on ethics committees. It includes a discussion of structural as well as substantive issues faced by committees. There is a review of the history of bioethics, the nature of ethical decision making in the hospital, and legal issues of interest to committees.*
Weir, R. *Selective Nontreatment of Handicapped Newborns: Moral Dilemmas in Neonatal Medicine.* New York: Oxford University Press, 1984. *This book is the first serious treatment of ethical dilemmas of neonatal medicine, and it presents a balanced, coherent analysis of the medical, ethical, and legal arguments put forth to date. Numerous case studies highlight the broad range of cases involved.*

Newsletters/Journals

Ethical Currents. (Published quarterly by the Center for Bioethics, St. Joseph Health System, and the California Association of Catholic Hospitals) CACH, 1121 L Street, Suite 409, Sacramento, CA 95814. This newsletter is written particularly for members of ethics committees.
Hastings Center Report. (Published bimonthly) Institute of Society, Ethics and the Life Sciences, 360 Broadway, Hastings-on-Hudson, NY 10706.
Lineacre Quarterly, A Journal of the Philosophy and Ethics of Medical Practice. (Quarterly) The National Federation of Catholic Physicians Guilds, 850 Elm Grove Road, Elm Grove, WI 53122.

Bibliographies

BioethicsLine, National Library of Medical Data Base, Medlars Management. BioethicsLine *provides bibliographic information on questions of ethics and public policy arising in health care or biomedical research. Developed at the Center for Bioethics, Kennedy Institute of Ethics, Georgetown University, Bioethics-Line contains English language citations to material published from 1973 to the present. It is available through most libraries.*

Cornelius J. van der Poel, C.S.Sp.

Professionalism in Chaplaincy

We live in an age of specialization where people concentrate on a particular segment of knowledge or ability. One specific ability or one field of knowledge is developed to the highest possible degree, while other talents evolve according to their need and usefulness in support of one's major interest. We call this "professional development." Each field is its own profession. Thus, medicine, nursing, physiotherapy, pharmacy, etc. are all different professions, because they all focus on a special aspect of health care. In many points they overlap, complement and support each other, but in the final analysis each one has its own terrain. However, the more one wants to develop in one profession, the more one needs to know about other supportive fields of knowledge.

Pastoral ministry is no exception to this rule. As ministers we are particularly concerned with the individual's relationship with God. In other words, our field of professionalism lies in the realm of the spiritual. But it is a spiritual concern of a special kind. Pastoral ministry is not an abstract reflection on the nature of spiritual life or on the meaning of virtue and spiritual progress. It is, rather, a concrete relationship between two people with the purpose of assisting each other in their search for God. This mutual assistance is carried out under circumstances in which one of the participants suffers a physical or emotional imbalance which asks for special support and guidance, and in which the other participant has been trained to give this kind of guidance. The pastoral minister is involved in a special profession which deals with people who require particular support and guidance in their situations of pain and stress. Therefore the pastoral minister needs to be acquainted with the structure of the human personality and with human emotional development. Furthermore, the pastoral minister is often employed by a hospital or other health care institution. This makes him or her a member of an institutional organization which may not always be in full agreement with the spiritual values or perspectives of human dignity held by the churches. Nonetheless, pastoral ministry is a profession in its own right and asks for a professionalism with its own characteristics.

Most churches have been (and still are) hesitant to use the word "professionalism" for their day-to-day ministry and spiritual care. Perhaps this is because the word "professionalism" sounds too worldly and is too measurable to reflect the true meaning and sanctity of spiritual guidance. Perhaps it is because pastoral and spiritual care have no prominent place on the competitive job market. It is hardly conceivable that a pastor will be awarded a higher salary because of his extra training in spiritual theology. Yet there is a need among the ministers to be recognized as professionals, and, in our age of specialization, diplomas and certificates are very important. Thus, we see the development of the interesting phenomenon that professionalism in pastoral and spiritual care tends to be equated with the degree of training and proficiency in such related fields as psychology, sociology and others. We want to be called professionals, but too often our professionalism is expected to manifest itself in fields other than the spiritual. This may be likened to the evaluating of a physician's professionalism by the depth of his knowledge of nursing care and pharmacology. As pastoral workers we have not yet found the balance between our essentially spiritual task and the required and recognized knowledge of the human condition. We need to reflect seriously on the meaning of our professionalism as pastoral ministers or chaplains.

The Human Vocation: Oneness in Complexity

We will never be able to fathom the mystery of creation in which God crowned the array of existing creatures with the appearance of human life, a life that is called to be and to manifest God's own image and likeness. This mysterious existence unites the infinitude of divine life with creaturely finiteness. By its nature it brings together the eternal with the temporal, the immeasurable with material limitations. It is called to manifest, in created and visible activity, the uncreated and invisible reality of the divine life. At the heart of human existence lies a secret more incomprehensible than the bewildering magnitude of the depths of the oceans or the endless vastness of the galaxies. Yet this is the human mystery, because "created in the image of God" also means being called to share in God's life. Human life joins and integrates what seems mutually exclusive.

Daily experience tells us how our bodily condition is at the center of our being. The awareness of life, the relationship to our surroundings (our presence in a forest or city, with two feet on the earth or flying high above the land), is all measured by our bodily location. Even relationships to other persons, exchange of ideas, expression of feelings, sharing of joys, consolation in sadness and support in needs are only possible through some form of bodily interaction. The human vocation of manifesting the image of God is essentially spiritual, but it cannot be realized in human life except through a co-constituent existence of the body.

The responsibilities which the human vocation places upon each individual and upon society cannot be fulfilled without bodily activity. Our sense of personal needs depends greatly on the way we see and experience ourselves. An individual's self-image is closely related to his or her body image. Everyone has dreams of what he or she would like to be. Being heavier or lighter, taller or smaller, than others influences how we feel about ourselves. To be sick or to lose a limb may demand a readjustment to life in which the individual must rise above one's prior attachment to physical appearance and come to grips with one's present condition. Without such personal readjustment there can be no inner peace, and one's relationship to society will be colored by the value which one ascribes to one's own person and to one's abilities.

It is obviously unavoidable that the bodily condition in which we live influences our relationship with God. God created us to live in this material/spiritual existence. He did not create us as two independent elements, body and soul, that are glued together. He did not create the body as a prison in which the spirit is temporarily contained. Nor is the body a tool through which the human spirit can act and seek perfection. Rather, we are such an inseparable unity that spirit and body have no independent existence. The human is utterly destroyed if one aspect is missing. Thus, worship of God is not just a spiritual matter. Bodily expression places worship in time and space. Bodily involvement makes any constructive human activity a participation in the process of creation, which is the continuous unfolding of God's self-manifestation.

Here we touch at the heart of the integrative dimension that makes the human reality fully human. The integration of material and spiritual values intensifies the human participation in cosmic growth and development, since it reaches beyond material existence into the realm of the spiritual. It makes the spiritual visible and recognizable in a material world without violating the true nature of either. The interaction between the material and the spiritual in human life is such that the one cannot be understood without the other. Simultaneously, it places human life in such a depth of mystery that Vatican Council II stated in the *Pastoral Constitution on the Church in the Modern World:* "In reality, it is only in the mystery of the Word made flesh that the mystery of human existence truly becomes clear" (n. 22).

The pastoral minister has the privileged and sensitive task of assisting in the unfolding of this mystery at the most critical moments of human life. When human support systems fail and when happenings in daily experience become incomprehensible, it is his or her responsibility to find a way through the labyrinth of disappointments to a new wholeness of life. It is a journey to a wholeness in which the relationship to God and to spiritual values plays a major role.

In describing the healing miracles of Jesus, the evangelists frequently use the expression: "Your faith has healed you." This is clearly stated in the story of the woman who suffered from a hemorrhage (Mk 5:34). Jesus commended the faith of the paralyzed man and his friends who let him down through the roof in front of him. "Seeing their faith Jesus said, 'My friend, your sins are forgiven you' " (Lk 5:20). In these instances in which adult responsible personalities search for wholeness, there is a relationship between their personal faith and the healing action of Jesus. The Lord seems to work in conjunction with the human disposition. This connection is understandable, since the human is created in the image of God, i.e. called to live the life of the infinite in created reality. God's interaction with the human is bound to be shaped by the qualities and dispositions of each individual.

It is rather easy to see that faith, hope and love are requirements in every human relationship with God. It is also easy to accept that the depth of our relationship with God is very closely connected with the depth of our faith, hope or love. It is more complicated to grasp how the very existence and form of these same virtues of faith, hope and love depend to a large extent on the personality of the individual believer. Yet this is an inescapable fact. These virtues are divine gifts to the individual person, but they are also a personal expression and can be received and lived only through personal qualities. Perhaps it would be more accurate to say that all virtues are gifts which come to life in the reality of human existence, rather than being given to the human from the outside. Faith, love and any other virtue remain abstract concepts until they take shape in concrete human existence. This means that every individual has a personal call from God. It also means that a special responsibility is placed on the minister who must guide others with truly pastoral concern.

Where Human and Divine Interact

The common expressions that "faith is a gift of God" and that "God bestows his grace upon us" are undoubtedly true, but they are also confusing and deceptive. They give the impression that faith and grace are additions to an already complete and pre-existing reality, but that, in fact, these qualities do not belong to the human condition. Such an impression is inaccurate. Faith and grace, together with other essential virtues, are part and parcel of human wholeness. The human is created in the image of God. This does not mean that the human is merely a receptacle into which God's image can be poured. It means, rather, that the human is an existence which reaches its fullness only when God's image is present and reflected in the limited capacities of the person in his or her interpersonal setting.

This integrative perspective is enormously important for our understanding of spiritual life and for the form of our pastoral approach. A brief reflection on the nature of the usual Christian triad of faith, hope and love may clarify this.

Faith is not only an intellectual adherence to a statement that is not fully understood and that is accepted on the authority of a trustworthy person, but it is also a response to an inner need that is awakened by the statement and that now is allowed to guide our inclinations and behavior. Daily human life is an example of this. The acknowledgment of personal value and dignity is an inner need of every person. The affirmation of this personal value by another not only awakens and strengthens this need, it also allows this knowledge to influence the individual's behavior. We can transfer this concept to the area of faith.

Since humanity is created in the image of God, there is an inner need to commit oneself to God, who is the completion and wholeness of our human existence. When statements about God touch the inner depth and find an echo in this existing need, they become the guide for the individual's behavior. I do not intend to "humanize" the life of faith and to eliminate all divine influence. The opposite is true. Human life is called to share in the divine life. This call itself is God's gift, and in this gift lies the source and potential to respond appropriately. God's gift is innate to the human. To respond to God's gift is to be deeply human and, simultaneously, to manifest the divine.

Another consequence flows forth from this human condition. The divine life grows within us in the shape and form in which our human life develops. The need for God responds to the deepest need for personal value and dignity. However, the vision of personal value and dignity is greatly influenced by the earliest human experiences. The child born into a family in which love and mutual respect are the normal way of life will develop a different image and respect for himself or herself than the child whose earliest surroundings were filled with disagreement, mutual disrespect or hatred. The early experience of rejection closes the personality from trust and love. A deep understanding of the structure of the human personality will, therefore, help also to comprehend the differentiation of faith among different individuals. Knowledge of psychology does not give one the power to bring faith to people, but it does help to see some characteristics of the faith expression in individuals. This knowledge can assist in making faith more personal, and, in some instances, it may reveal certain obstacles in the development of faith.

The second leg of the triad, the virtue of hope, is equally a gift of God that grows and is shaped in the human reality. Hope is trust in the divine promise, but this trust is cast in human form. Hope is based upon faith, in which the knowledge of the divine life is grasped according to human capacities. This understanding is interwoven with a vision of our own human limitations and with a recognition of our own human limitations and with a recognition of our human inability to be what God has called us to be. Instead of despairing in the face of the all-holy, the human clings to the promise of God that he will give what is needed to live this human life to the best of our strengths. People believe that this effort is an acceptable manifestation of God's life in us. In the form and in the development of hope, the human personality structure plays an important role. The person who never experienced trust will find it exceptionally difficult to trust God. For such persons trustworthiness must be proven by immediate and constant satisfaction. Very different is the individual who grew up in a trusting environment. He or she will feel at ease to let go into the hands of another. This person can surrender and be at peace.

In this context, we can see how hope flows over into love. The ability to surrender oneself to another is an essential foundation for a complete surrender to God. To surrender is a unifying action. It allows the two persons to flow into each other because of their mutual acceptance, appreciation and respect. In this mutual gift, neither giver nor receiver suffers a loss. On the contrary, because of generosity without possessiveness, each individual becomes more independent through the richness of the other. Love is as wide and deep as the personality, yet it goes beyond human measures. It is the gift of self into the depth of another and the reception of the other into one's own depth. Obviously the individual personalities play an essential role here. Both giving and receiving can only be done according to the abilities and qualities of the persons involved. God asks honesty in giving and in responding. He asks that each person give and respond according to his or her own abilities. The ability to love God is, itself, God's gift, but through God's gift this ability has become a human quality. It is a human quality that can be developed and can grow through human efforts which are simultaneously inspired and carried by God's love for us. It is an inextricable interwovenness that, nonetheless, is greatly aided by human understanding, acceptance and respect. The more the human love develops, the more the divine love can manifest itself in human life and behavior. In love, the divine and the human blend into a union that surpasses all comprehension.

My repeated reference to psychological factors for the form and growth of Christian/divine virtues does not mean that I consider the degree of professionalism in the pastoral minister to be in proportion to his or her knowledge of psychology. Far from it! Spiritual depth goes far beyond psychological dimensions. While spiritual guidance cannot be achieved merely by psychological counseling, pastoral ministry cannot be effective without a certain degree of knowledge of the human psyche and human emotional life. Nor can it be effective without knowledge of spiritual life and spiritual experience. In the final analysis, *pastoral professionalism consists of the ability to integrate spiritual doctrine, values and experiences with the human factors of daily life.* It is a professionalism of a unique kind, demanding in the minister an integration of spiritual depth, intellectual insight and human sensitivity. It is a kind of professionalism that is not exercised on people, but that reaches out to people. Spiritual knowledge or progress is not something that one can pass on to others. It is something that one can share with other persons, and in this sharing both benefit and grow. Pastoral ministry is the celebration of the Christ-life in the community of believers.

This celebration happens in many ways. It can be the realization of the compassionate Christ who understands human suffering and responds by conveying to the suffering person the courage and strength to make this suffering part of his or her life. In this process of the patient's self-surrender in which the minister plays a role, the minister becomes also more deeply rooted in Christ. It can be the celebration of the forgiving Christ who reaches out to the sinner, whom he invites through loving concern into a renewed union with him. Pastoral ministry itself is a sacramental activity in which the personal presence in concern, dedication and love is the external visibility of the divine mystery that is made real through it. Perhaps it is possible to explain this more clearly in a reflection on the grace-giving relationship in what is usually called "sacramental ministry." Let us take the sacrament of the anointing of the sick as an example.

During the last few decades our understanding of "sacrament" has deepened considerably. The past emphasized the sacred "rite" in which the life of grace was given and strengthened. Present insights prefer to place greater emphasis on the reality of the mystery of Christ's presence which is manifested in the celebration of the sacrament. The sacrament is understood more as a celebration of the mystery of Christ's presence than as the performance of a sacred rite through which graces are communicated. The importance and meaningfulness of the rite depends on the degree to which it is filled with the reality of the mystery. In this perspective, the human participation receives a greater importance. The deeper the faith of the participants, the more will the celebration be the external expression of the mystery itself.

I start from the assumption that we have reached well beyond the stage in which the anointing was understood as the "extreme unction." During and after Vatican Council II this has become much clearer. It is called the "anointing of the sick" to convey, by the name itself, the message that this sacrament is meant to be celebrated while the sick person is as fully aware as possible of his or her situation. It is a celebration in which the community unites in faith and prayer with the suffering person.

In this mystery celebration, three perspectives of essential importance are inseparably interwoven. (1) The human person is created in the image of God and finds his or her fullness by living out in created reality the invisible and infinite presence of the divine. (2) The human person can live and develop fully only in constructive interhuman relationships. Constructive interhuman exchange is the external dimension of God's creative self-giving. In the broad sense of the word, it is sacramental. (3) The sacraments of the church, which are the signs of God's redemptive grace, are the human celebration of the mystery of Christ's presence in the various conditions and circumstances of human life.

One of the mysteries of Christ's presence among us was his redemptive suffering. Suffering is never a desirable condition. Even the Lord himself asked the Father to let this chalice pass him by. But he was willing to face up to any hardship of life that the Father asked of him. What the Father asked was the deepest recognition of the total human dependence on God, and the acceptance of a spiritual consecration to God as the center and fulfillment of human life. Responding to this call, Jesus said: "Into your hands, Father, I commend my spirit." This total surrender was the redemptive factor in Jesus' life, in his suffering, in his death and resurrection. At no point in created history has there been a moment in which the integrative wholeness of human existence was more perfect than when Christ gave himself in total surrender to the Father while he was dying upon the cross. Completely separated from any form of human support, he entrusted his total being to the Father. In this total surrender, he also gained total union and eternal life with the Father. What he had by divine nature he gained in his human surrender.

The sacrament of the anointing of the sick celebrates that mystery of the suffering and surrendering Christ. The sacrament is intended for persons whose illness seriously impedes their normal way of living and which may lead to the completion of life in death. For these persons, the human support systems on which they relied seem to fall away. Their balance and wholeness of life is broken. The external sources of strength are withdrawn and earlier expectations do not work out.

In this search for a new balance, they need to develop a perspective of life that otherwise may remain in the background: the power of interhuman relationships and of reliance on God. Human reliance on God in health is characterized by the grateful use of one's talents and of human friendship relationships. Reliance on God in illness is of a different nature. Its main characteristic is a sense of weakness and human insufficiency. Often this is accompanied by a feeling of personal uselessness. But in this experience the patient must find the conviction of faith that in the total dependence on God lies also the deepest truth of one's human existence. To the degree that human support systems ebb away, we must rely on support from others. In the experience of dependence on others, the human dependence on God is made visible, while, reciprocally, the experience of the dependence on God is made visible in interhuman dependence.

Ministry and Sacramentality

It is at this point in the process of human relationship and growth that the minister must show himself or herself to be pastoral and professional in the fullest sense of the word. The pastoral dimension is manifested in a deep respect for the dignity of each person and in the genuine concern for the spiritual values in the patient's life. Psychological dimensions show forth in the depth of empathy, sensitivity and understanding of the human reality of pain, anxiety and uncertainty, realities which need to be integrated with the spiritual needs and desires of the individual. Pastoral and psychological dimensions together form a unique professionalism that unites psycho-emotional and spiritual factors into an inseparable oneness. This professionalism is directed to the special goal of helping a sick person to place his or her life in total service of God. This professionalism is eminently pastoral in that it fully respects the freedom and personal responsibility of the patient, while it guides the patient in his or her union with God.

Illness is not only the sign of human limitation and of the transitory condition of human life, but it can also be the sign of total dependence on God and, therefore, an opportunity for total surrender to him. To unite with the suffering Christ is to reinstate a wholeness in life which is based upon dependence on God and on surrender to the Father. Thus human illness is a call to recognize and live out the mystery of the suffering Christ. Patients participate in this mystery when, in faith and surrender, they celebrate the sacrament of the anointing.

Illness also signals the human community's total dependence on God. In the care for the sick, the community unites itself with the suffering, surrendering Christ and celebrates this mystery with the patient. Thus Christ's presence comes to life and is concretely experienced in the encounter of minister and patient through the power of this sacramental celebration.

In the celebration of the sacrament, the human reality and wholeness is expressed in ways that are otherwise impossible. On the one hand, the presence and involvement of the minister draws the community into the world of the patient. On the other hand, it makes the suffering of the patient a communal experience through faith and prayer. Interhuman concern is clearly expressed; dependence on the divine and spiritual values in human life becomes the center of attention and the aim of human activity. The lives of all who are present open up to the Lord's influence. The recognition of weakness and limitation enters more deeply into human awareness, and surrender to God becomes the heart of human dedication. The sacrament of anointing is not merely a source of strength for the patient; it is the celebration of the mystery of Christ's suffering in the community as a whole. It is a sharing in the life of Christ, and thus it is a source of grace for all who participate in it.

Other sacraments, too, give an actual sharing in Christ's life with us and are a source of strength and spiritual growth for minister and patient alike. Take, for example, the eucharist. If we reflect again on the definition of "sacrament" as the celebration of the mystery of Christ's presence with us, then the eucharist will be seen as the mystery of communicating and sharing the Christ-life. In a way, it is much easier and much more comfortable to see the eucharist as the coming of Christ to us with his grace and strength. From this perspective, Christ comes to us, as it were, from the outside. He becomes our main support, but in a sense he remains an "added" support that surpasses our human condition. However valid this perspective may be, there is a deeper significance of eucharist.

The eucharist is the celebration of Christ's life among us. This means that we share, in our limited human way and according to our personal abilities, in the Lord's dedication to the Father. His presence is a creative presence which gives existence where it was not and which brings to fruition what is in the process of unfolding. His presence is also a redemptive presence that enables individuals and community to allow in their lives the deep unselfish love that seeks the growth of total surrender to God in oneself and in others. Both the creative and the redemptive presence presuppose an interhuman exchange based upon faith in God and upon concern for others. Faith in God is the internal need which is touched by knowledge of God coming in from the outside, and now becoming a source of life and behavior. The interhuman concern is the concrete realization of Christ's reaching out in a love that is life-giving, supporting and building.

The celebration of the eucharist is the visible and sacramental participation in the life of Christ. It celebrates the reality of Christ's total self-giving and of the complete human dedication of oneself to one another in Christ. This unreserved self-giving becomes particularly meaningful in illness. When human strengths and support systems retreat to the background and prove their limitations, reliance on Christ and the conscious participation in his death and resurrection obtain a special significance. This is undoubtedly to the benefit of the patient. Since the minister of the eucharist establishes the visibility of Christ's reaching out, the minister's understanding of the needs in the patient and the patient's faith-filled realization of the eucharistic gift unite in this human celebration the deepest response to emotional desires and spiritual growth. It is an eminent pastoral involvement and professionalism par excellence.

Pastoral professionalism is perhaps most evident in the sacrament of reconciliation. The understanding of human weakness, empathy and compassion lie at the heart of guiding human reunion with God. Reconciliation with God is very different from psychotherapy, but it is equally different from the interpretation of confession as the almost magical taking away of the spiritual residues of sinful activities and replacing them by grace-filled support systems. The sacrament of reconciliation celebrates the mystery in which a repentant, honest openness of sinful human existence reaches out to and unites with a loving reconciling God. It is a mystery that acknowledges human limitation and weakness, but in which dedication to God is accepted and lived, despite shortcomings. It is a new creation in which weakness is filled with strength and in which human limitations become the shape that hides and manifests the human striving for wholeness. This is of particular importance for the sick. Their life itself bears the signs of weakness and of dependence on others. Their life speaks of reliance on God and on self-realization within the parameters of brokenness. Sympathy and compassion are the human elements that provide support to those who are ill. Faith and trust in God create the condition that allows the person to live in integrated wholeness. Thus, the sacrament of reconciliation is the combination of human psychological and spiritual support that makes the ministry to the sick such an outstanding expression of professional involvement.

My discussion of the sacraments does not suggest that pastoral ministry is primarily a clergy-related occupation. Far from it. Human life itself is sacramental insofar that in the visibility of its existence lies the mystery of divine presence and love. The total mentality and undercurrent for the celebration of Jesus' suffering is already active in the compassionate relationship of any health care minister with a patient. The reality of the Christ-life among us in constructive human interchange is eucharistic by nature and finds a high point in the celebration of the eucharist. The ability to accept one's weakness and to develop a deeper sense of confidence in God is a form of reconciliation which is, primarily, a product of sensitive ministerial relationships. Every dimension of health care ministry participates in this search for wholeness by allowing the individual to integrate his or her human limitations into the concrete vocation of this moment in life. Health care ministry is meant to be a professional pastorate, but it can be so only if it is at the same time animated by a pastoral professionalism.

Some people may consider the preceding, largely theological, reflections as only remotely related to a professionalism that is required on the organizational level of health care institutions. It seems to me that they form the heart of the chaplain's professionalism. If institutions take the concern for human wholeness seriously, and if they accept that wholeness is not the same as physical health, then they will also accept that pastoral professionalism reaches far beyond administrative abilities. On the other hand, the chaplain who takes his task seriously needs to live this life of deep spiritual values which take into consideration the condition of the patient as well as the goals of the institution. Professionalism in chaplaincy and pastoral ministry is of a very special kind. It is called to fill the most discouraging human circumstances with the redemptive presence of a loving God. Many of its requirements cannot be learned in colleges or at a university, nor can they be fully reflected in job descriptions. They must result from an experience of God's presence and from an openness to God's self-manifestation in the weakness of human existence.

Margot Hover

========================

Marketing Pastoral Care

A colleague of mine relates a recent conversation with a local physician. "I became a doctor to work with people, and now I spend three quarters of my time doing paperwork," the doctor lamented. In turn, the chaplain shared his resistance to the amount of time involved in charting, committee work, and other new procedures for which the hospital's department of pastoral care had recently taken responsibility. "Perhaps you chaplains are at last having to face the realities that other helping professions faced long ago," the physician summarized with grim satisfaction.

What he was saying about the reality of paperwork could be said with equal validity about marketing. I should make it clear from the beginning that I am convinced that pastoral care departments must market themselves, even in denomination-sponsored hospitals, where they have generally been taken for granted. In fact, "taken for granted" constitutes an important reason for marketing, as I view health care systems and the ways they utilize (or scrap) chaplaincy services. I am familiar with pastoral care departments in public hospitals, where tax dollars (and non-revenue-producing services) were suddenly and drastically cut. I've listened to Catholic hospital administrators describe concepts of pastoral care that bore no resemblance to actual department goals and operations in their own institutions. And finally, I see the same handwriting on the walls that all of us in pastoral care see these days. The traditional pastoral care labor force is changing in age, preparation, motivation and lifestyle. As older chaplains retire, their replacements—often deacons and laity—are well-trained but plagued by ambiguous role definitions and nebulous ecclesiastical support.

All of this means that marketing can no longer be viewed as a worldly, frivolous enterprise for which hospital chaplains have no time. Pastoral care departments in public and for-profit hospitals are generally the first services to be cut when budgets must be trimmed or realigned to DRG standards. And even if denomination-sponsored

50

hospital administrators are seduced by the affirmation in patients' thanks for "the good sisters' visits," both the "good sisters" and the mislabeled lay and diaconal chaplains would appreciate recognition of their skill, dedication and training independent of their lifestyle.

This chapter will deal with the concept of marketing and with the application of one marketing model and strategy specifically to pastoral care. In this context, I define pastoral care as "faithful companionship provided to people in crisis as they work to integrate their own faith and value systems with the physical and emotional situations in which they find themselves." Pastoral caregivers have as the tools of their trade expertise in empathy, listening, confrontation, prayer leadership and theologizing, as well as the willingness and ability to continue on their own faith journey.

I define marketing in this article broadly as the process of identifying needs and resources and matching the two. Since the "product" provided by pastoral care departments is intangible and the results not as easily quantified as say, respiratory care or dietary services, marketing pastoral care necessarily involves considerable efforts at education and promotion.

Marketing

The notion of marketing when applied to religious issues and services is still often treated with ambivalence. Our city newspapers recently ran a full page advertisement for a local hospital that featured a picture of the hospital chaplain. The ad generated strong reactions both pro and con. Some ministers were jealous that they did not receive similar regard from their institutions; others resented the use of religion to sell a particular product—that hospital. Still others hailed this recognition of chaplains as professional colleagues along with the rest of the hospital staff.

My own institution somewhat unwittingly plunked itself squarely in the middle of the marketing arena when it created a decedent care position and function, and located it in the department of pastoral care. As a county hospital always operating at full capacity to serve the area indigent, Parkland Memorial Hospital seemingly has little need for marketing. Our department did, however. It was hoped that our claiming the decedent care function would make the department better known and utilized—even indispensable. It did, with other interesting side-effects, as well.

Under the decedent care program, a chaplain attends each death to render care to family and staff, to monitor the paperwork, and to oversee admission to and release from the morgue. Chaplains also facilitate county burial as well as smooth working relationships with the medical examiner and area funeral directors. Overnight, chaplains were written into nursing procedures, and accountability was demanded. If our chaplains lost the "other-worldly" status so often awarded clergy, they gained respect for their skill and willingness to "get their hands dirty." Staff trusted them with a wider range of feelings and problems, and chaplains spent more time on the units with them. And if chaplains are now "fair target" for the same anger, frustration and abruptness focused on other specialists in the high-stress hospital setting, chaplains are best able to provide another model for dealing with those feelings. Thus, they are tenacious, faithful, prophetic participants in the collisions and reconciliations that heretofore went on without pastoral care. And the department of pastoral care is no longer considered a helpful (expensive) extra.

Marketing as Project Design: Matching Needs with Responses

Our setting may be unique; each institution has its own unique needs and resources. Nevertheless, let's use that example as a case study in marketing pastoral care. First, what is marketing? I'll define it simply as the process of matching needs with responses. In today's changing health-care marketplace—and pastoral care is not exempt from either change or marketing—there is fierce competition to provide successful, cost-efficient matches. Our decedent care program grew out of a televised press conference following the crash of a jumbo jet, at which area funeral directors fought over the bodies of victims brought to our hospital. Our administrator vowed that families—and the hospital itself—would never again be subjected to such insult. There was the need.

A second case: during the 1970s business and industry began to recognize the magnitude in terms of time lost and insurance payments made because of health problems that could have been prevented—workplace accidents, substance abuse, overweight, for examples. There was the need.

A third case: in the early days of "certificates of need," one suburban midwestern hospital found itself pushed to define exactly what made its brand of care "just what the doctor ordered," as opposed to care promised at a proposed competing facility. There was the need.

A fourth case: in the face of a rapidly growing population of AIDS patients and their family members and friends, Parkland wanted to demonstrate its availability as a center of caring support as well as of medical expertise. There was the need.

Marketing means matching needs with responses. Marketing involves reaching into available resources to find answers for questions and solutions for problems. In the first situation, the pastoral care office capitalized on the chaplains' image as people already equipped to deal with death, to design a decedent care program to be administered through that office. That greatly reduced problems surrounding hospital death procedures, enhanced the chaplains' presence in the hospital, and contributed to the unique character of the hospital's clinical pastoral education program.

In the second situation, some corporations hired industrial chaplains to minister to employee stress. Others hired hospital-packaged programs, which often included physical, emotional and spiritual support personnel and approaches.

In the third situation, hospital administrators discovered already in place a pastoral care program that trained volunteers to call each patient within forty-eight hours after dismissal to see how the patient was progressing. The resulting body of patient feedback provided a profile of the way the hospital was perceived and utilized in the community.

And in the fourth situation, Parkland recognized the role that area churches played in the community ministry among AIDS victims, and matched that to a specific position in the pastoral care department, one of the first in the country to fund an AIDS chaplain.

All of these involved the creative matching of uniquely pastoral resources with needs that cry for a pastoral response. So marketing has more to do with pastoral care than making sure that a crucifix hangs in the hospital lobby, that mass times appear correctly on the Saturday tray cards, and that each nursing unit sends a representative to the Respect Life or Pastoral Care Week planning committee. Rev. Douglas A. Morrison (*Health Progress,* October 1984) sees that pastoral care personnel have a prophetic role, exercised when they are motivated by love to look creatively and critically at both inadequacies and resources within their departments as well as within their institutions. He envisions a pastoral care team that courageously and compassionately undertakes departmental and institutional self-evaluation and collaboration with other prophets within both the institution and the larger community. Walter Brueggemann writes that "it is the vocation of the prophet to keep alive the ministry of imagination" (*The Prophetic Imagination*. Fortress Press, 1978). When James asked, "Are there any among you who are sick?" (Jas 5:14) he was throwing the doors open to amazing possibility. And he was also asking a marketing question: "What do you need?"

William D. Novelli has designed a six-stage process model for marketing associations that lends itself to the marketing of pastoral care (paper presented to the American Society of Association Executives, 1983). The first stage focuses on an analysis—of the market as a whole, of the individual consumers, of the organization and community structure in which the department operates. For instance, who are the people that chaplains at Holy Patience Hospital could serve? Patients, their families, and staff, for starters. As hospitals become centers for critical care, however, another population develops in outpatient and home care programs, requiring pastoral care-givers to think more aggressively about outreach. Local pastors are surprisingly influential in the choices their parishioners make; how can *they* be served by pastoral care departments? Community involvement: are chaplains involved on a variety of levels with other community agencies, foundations and civic groups? Visibility within affiliated institutions: have chaplains applied for faculty status in schools of medicine, nursing and health-related professions? Media: are pastoral care providers approached by journalists for their insights on health care, spiritual values, ethical issues, and family dynamics?

The goal of this type of analysis, of course, is to uncover needs which chaplains could address, so that the department is not only useful but indispensable to the hospital and the community it serves. You might involve your department and the department advisory board in brainstorming to identify all of the groups that constitute your "market," consumers of the services you can provide. Become aware both of the special character of each group and of existing institutional goals and taboos. For instance, in a drive to demonstrate fiscal belt-tightening, one hospital administrator "red-flagged" pastoral care department fliers dealing with family needs, choosing instead to emphasize an intensive focus on patients alone. In one municipal hospital, a department of pastoral care was set up with the specific goal of community outreach to overcome citizen resistance to the new facility. Both of these cases illustrate the types of information that are important in formulating a profile of the market.

The second stage in the marketing process is planning a specific formula for action. That blueprint must include realistic objectives that are broad enough to be challenging, and narrow enough to be achieved and evaluated. These objectives should generally be quantified. Our quality assurance consultants wouldn't let us get away with: "To provide the best pastoral care possible." In contrast, "To visit the mother of each newborn or fetal demise" readily lent itself to a plan of action and evaluation. The chaplain's visit could then be correlated to the rate at which mothers returned for clinic follow-up or to the accuracy of documentation for county burial. Both of those outcomes would contribute to hospital goals for quality health care for the indigent in our service area, and would enhance the department's reputation in the hospital and community.

Marketing objectives may involve or even focus on working out collaborations among existing services. Our OB nurses derived much personal satisfaction from providing emotional support to mothers who lost babies, and they were wary of encroachments from chaplains. The gap of suspicion was bridged when chaplains began to support mothers as they viewed their babies' bodies and made funeral plans, both appropriate complements to the nurses' role in our institution. The marketing of our department benefited when nurses traded their territorial issues for the opportunity to see chaplains as spiritual support—not only for their patients but for themselves.

Another example: area clergy can be reached by hospital-sponsored seminars and luncheon workshops on listening skills and grief. But a pastoral care department could market itself to two groups at once by bringing together clergy and physicians to discuss the specific emotional and spiritual needs of cardiac, AIDS, stroke and cancer patients. Or could your department use Pastoral Care Week to market itself to hospital employees by organizing a Wellness Fair with booths on various religious denominations as well as attractive displays and activities from other departments on stress, nutrition and health checks?

Once objectives have been set and action plans developed, it is time to enter phase three, where the plan is mapped out, tested, refined and finally set in place. Hospitals are such intricate organizations that getting input can be risky business. But if one can run the risk of having one's balloon pricked, it is better to do that now than later. Each year, our department is asked to prepare a booth or presentation for the annual meeting of the coalition that provides our funding. Their hopes that we will bring an impressive production are matched by their fears that we will disappoint or embarrass them before present and potential donors. For our part, we harbor matching fears. We are still searching for ways to allay all of those feelings without violating needs for creativity or control. We should definitely keep working at it, however, for that step is a crucial phase of any marketing program. What we need is a test market or trial run for our presentation.

Similarly with the other examples I've given. Before our decedent care program was designed, and then before it was set in place, we solicited in-depth feedback from every department that would be affected. We designed training programs on the new procedures for chaplains, nurses and administrators, and we negotiated for time on orientation programs and continuing education agendas.

At one point, I had a brainstorm about our department's sponsoring a program on AIDS for local funeral directors. It would require a minimum investment of my time, merely lining up the program and arranging for use of the print shop and Board of Morticians mailing labels. The need surfaced when morticians increasingly used chaplains to vent their fears about contracting AIDS and their frustrations with the complicated family dynamics often surrounding AIDS cases. Having analyzed the "market" and planned my approach, I tried out my idea on several hospital personnel from other departments. I discovered that Infection Control had proposed a similar program several years before, but had not been able to raise any interest. Forewarned, I knew I would have to capitalize on the "consumer's" personal contact with chaplains to influence them to attend, or think of other ways of getting the program content to that audience. Whatever format the program finally takes, there will be three benefits. As their fears and suspicions are alleviated, funeral directors' work with AIDS patients and their families is bound to be more empathic and supportive. Our pastoral care department will be seen as a knowledgeable and compassionate resource for the community outside our walls. And administrators in our hospital will see that pastoral care is an active community asset, especially important for a public tax-supported facility.

Again, as the program plans are developed and tested, it is important to ferret out all of the taboos and hidden agendas that might collide with it. For instance, I had no idea that the administrator mentioned earlier objected to the department's work with families until I heard his reaction to an interview I had given to the hospital's in-house newsletter. That factor was crucial in our subsequent choices about programs and publicity. As painful as it is to hear criticism of a "pet" project, it is easier and better to get feedback from as many sectors as possible during this early phase.

The fourth step is implementation. As your plan is executed, it is important that all the work of the initial phases be well integrated so that the project can succeed. If you've designed seasonal prayer cards to be placed on patients' supper trays, for instance, have you gained the cooperation of the tray line workers? Frequent monitoring is essential if you are not to arrive at the end of Lent with boxes of unused cards. Is Housekeeping still checking bedstands to make sure each one contains a New Testament? Do the housekeepers know where to find replacement copies? Who checks to make sure these are reordered? Are the Bibles available to staff, and are all staff members aware of that? Are announcements about chapel services always made coherently and on time? If area clergy are urged to visit their parishioners in the hospital, are they able to find room numbers—at all hours? And does the hospital staff know that area ministers have been invited so that they can join the effort to make neighboring clergy feel a part of the patient's total care?

The fifth step in the marketing process is to evaluate the effectiveness of the "product." Collect data on the outcomes, then match that data against your original objectives. If your original goal was to provide a Bible for each patient, it is unfair to judge the program a failure if few of the patients actually read the scriptures. More "hidden agendas" may surface during this stage. While the stated objective of our decedent care program may have been to facilitate families' journeys through the system, I've sometimes wondered if we really hoped to banish death itself from the system. It is always good to allow those unspoken expectations to surface, but they should be channeled into the next step rather than used to measure the present project.

Evaluating pastoral care in many institutions is different from evaluating other departments and projects, too. Quantifying pastoral care results requires a different mind-set than most hospitals are used to. Suppose that the project objective was to have a chaplain check with the head nurse on each unit each day for referrals. Nurses are sometimes more apt to slide over a chaplain's performance with, "Well, he doesn't come *every* day, but we know he's busy," than they would in evaluating a respiratory therapist, for example. Some hospitals with clinical pastoral education programs have begun to build a research component into their training, where students are pushed to define exactly what they do, and exactly what benefits patients reap from pastoral visitation. This type of data is crucial for the growing number of hospitals where decisions are made on the basis of dollar effectiveness. That kind of approach is long overdue.

Finally, the sixth stage of this process centers on channeling feedback into stage one of the cycle. Analysis is repeated, this time with a more extensive body of information than was available the first

time through. For instance, in working through a project on pastoral
care's use of the hospital's closed circuit TV network, you may have
discovered or collected data that would help you to address the
problem of small viewing audiences at Sunday mass telecasts. On the
issue of organ donation: while I feel that chaplains' role in the organ
donation process should be as supportive mediator for the family,
and never as solicitor, statistics suggest that clergy involvement increases retrieval rate. Can you document the correlation in your
hospital, perhaps making a case for including the chaplain in every
family conference where this topic is discussed? State by state, laws
are being passed requiring that patients be approached on admission
to consider organ donation. Pastoral involvement on behalf of the
family is quite appropriate, and, once again, it would enhance the
credibility and visibility of chaplains as equal professionals on the
health care team. All of these examples lend themselves to this six-
phase process of systematic problem solving—matching of needs and
resources—marketing!

Marketing as Promotion

I am aware that this runs counter both to the popular notion of
marketing as putting up billboards and posters and to the traditional
position that pastoral care needs no marketing. In today's shifting
medical economy, survival of departments that do not produce reve-
nue is a real question. More important than that, however, is the
danger that pastoral care's contribution to the achievement of a hospital's mission is not valued because it has not been defined or described in terms that make sense to administrators who must balance
the institutional checkbook each month. Ironically, there is a rapidly
growing body of research in the "soft" sciences that indicates that
our work as chaplains *can* be quantified and its value concretely
documented.

The chances are even that much of the work of a pastoral care
department may go unrecognized by the rest of the hospital staff. It's
frustrating to finish a long night's duty only to be greeted by a nurse's
bright "Do you work here?" or "Is this your regular job?" And so,
once again, I stress the importance of marketing both to administration and to parallel levels in the hospital.

Thus far I've dealt with the subject of marketing pastoral care in
terms of a needs-response, project approach to the various groups we
serve. It is also appropriate to examine the issue of marketing as

promotion. I am reminded of the parents of a four year old child who was dying of leukemia. The normal ambiguity of their grief process —hope amid resignation—was further complicated by the fragmented messages given by the steady stream of medical experts who filed through the hospital room. The respiratory therapist said that the child was adjusting well to the respirator. The oncologist noted the color of her toes and said her circulation was good. The nutritionist figured on her calculator that the little girl was getting adequate calories, and the physical therapist explained exercises that would maintain flexibility and muscle tone. How were the parents to understand, amid all this good news, the inescapable reality that their daughter was dying? There, the chaplain's presence served to help them maintain their focus on the whole picture and the meanings of their minutes together, rather than on the unrelated fragments of medical detail.

In the same way, chaplains serve as a reminder of the ultimate purpose of a health care institution. Pastoral care pulls together the fragments of an increasingly complex constellation of medical services and specialities around a center of the spiritual values and priorities of the patient. That is, it does if anyone knows it's there. Both by presence and by action, chaplains can serve to keep an institution in touch with the primary reasons for its existence—but only if they have visibility and credibility there.

How is that image built and maintained? By quality marketing efforts. For instance, what image is conveyed by the handwritten posters advertising Holy Week services? How often have your department fliers, brochures, and signs been designed in collaboration with hospital departments that are already expert in that kind of work—medical illustration, public relations, and the print shop, for example? It may cost money to have programs and brochures typeset, but a homespun publicity campaign communicates the idea that a program will be homespun, too. Few professionals have time to waste on that caliber of workshop.

It would be worthwhile to brainstorm within your department about the image you already project, and about the avenues available within the institution and community for building the kind of image necessary for the impact you want to have. Consider some of the following questions: Is your department phone extension listed in the telephone directory? Are the pastoral care offices readily accessible to the public? Are they listed on lobby signage? Does the department have its own newsletter? Do members contribute to other department newsletters? For example, our surgery patient care center publishes "Sutures," a monthly newsletter for its nurses, to which the chaplains contribute articles on stress, grief, chaplain profiles, and descriptions of the training programs offered through the department of pastoral care.

Is chaplaincy allotted time on the orientation schedule for new nurses? Are new administrators and staff doctors personally oriented to the department of pastoral care? If your hospital is a CPE center, have administrators ever accompanied the students and supervisors on pastoral rounds? Do they ever attend verbatim sessions? One can safely assume that administrators are familiar with licensing requirements for respiratory and physical therapists. They are generally not familiar with certification standards for chaplains or with accreditation requirements for CPE training centers, and therefore may sometimes assume that fervor is an adequate substitute for skill when it comes to pastoral care. All the more need for marketing here.

Our CEO meets personally with all new chaplains and students because he knows the pastoral care program is important. Or is it the other way around—he knows the program is important because he himself is asked to meet personally with all new members? And our department recently created a major impact in our hospital when we requested a time slot on the schedule for the most recent Joint Commission on the Accreditation of Hospitals (JCAH) review. Pastoral care had always been exempt from the bustle and strain of other departments as they rushed to document their compliance with standards. Now, not only are we unafraid of scrutiny, but we are eager to demonstrate that our procedures, policies and records are as professional as any other service in the institution.

Hospitals that serve as teaching institutions have yet another arena for marketing department services and personnel. Chaplains generally give the invocation at graduation ceremonies. But are chaplains ever awarded faculty status? Chaplains are experts in religious processes and values and the ways these function for individuals and families in the throes of a hospitalization. Those topics may be given only cursory treatment, if they are handled at all in educational programs for health care professionals. Do the chaplains in your department believe in themselves enough to offer their skill and insights to students?

And speaking of education, do department members' achievements receive the same recognition accorded to members of other departments? Are they mentioned in house publications when they publish articles, finish degrees or receive awards? Are they encouraged to serve actively on committees and boards?

I was tempted to slide by the standard questions of time: "Where will I find time to do all that? I'm happy simply visiting patients." I don't mean to sound glib when I say that we are entering an era when we have little choice. If we overlook the task of marketing, of proving our value both to patients and to our institutions, we cannot be surprised when they opt for approaches and programs that do not include us.

In this chapter I've dealt with marketing both as promotion and as project design. I advocate an active approach, urging chaplains and directors of pastoral care to address on their terms those with power, both within and outside the institution. There is more at stake here than our accessibility and effectiveness with patients. At risk is the very survival of institutional pastoral care.

II. Pastoral Service

James Buryska

Pastoral Care Administration

In making some observations about the organization and administration of pastoral services in health care, it is my intention to take the following approach:

1. to begin with several assumptions about the present character, environment and circumstances of pastoral care; and, based on those assumptions,

2. to set down some general principles or qualities important in the management of pastoral services; and, finally,

3. to outline task priorities for those whose responsibility it is to organize and coordinate pastoral work in the institutional setting.

I am proceeding on the premise that the nature and characteristics of the work (i.e. providing pastoral services in the health care setting) will give a shape and character to its administration that is to some extent unique. Otherwise there would be little point in discussing the administration of pastoral services as distinct from that of any other hospital department or any other ecclesial ministry.

A few words about my use of terms. I use "chaplain" throughout to refer to the professional practitioner of pastoral care in a hospital or other health care institution. Other terms are perhaps fuller and more evocative, but "chaplain" is short, generic and widely understood. I use "pastoral care" to mean the providing of spiritual care by a recognized representative of a religious body, and occasionally to mean the organized department or other agency responsible for it. I use "hospital" broadly to refer to the health care facility, even though this may be a clinic, hospice, nursing home, or other institution. And, finally, I use "client," in spite of its clinical sound, to mean the recipient of care: client because, in addition to the patient, recipients of pastoral care may be family members, staff, or fellow chaplains.

The principles and tasks I will propose for the manager of pastoral care are based on the following assumptions about pastoral care itself:

1. Pastoral Care Functions at the Convergence of Three Systems: The Ecclesial, the Institutional and the Medical.

I picture pastoral ministry in a health care institution as the seat of a three-legged stool; the three legs are the church (in its broadest sense), the hospital, and the medical profession with its associated disciplines and technologies. Each of these "legs" or systems has its own identity with a set of values, priorities and premises particular to it. Furthermore, each has its own operational model or set of models prevalent at any given time as knowledge, tradition and current developments dictate.

From its roots in the church pastoral care receives its spiritual orientation, an openness to the transcendent and the readiness to address such intangible realities as salvation, sin and grace, and life beyond death. From the same source it also falls heir to an emphasis on tradition (in varying degrees), the assumption of a (usually hierarchical) structure generally based on ordination, and the supposition that the local church—the parish or congregation—is the primary focus and model of pastoral efforts. Another element of ecclesial influence is that of motivation. It is usual to find in those who serve in the name of the church some sense of a divine call to that service. Hence they are inclined to view their work as a vocation or ministry rather than simply as "a job" or a way of earning a living. Finally, the ecclesial base brings with it a dimension of community.

The institution in which pastoral care is practiced also has its influence. In spite of the recent inroads of Japanese management styles, there is normally a hierarchical organizational structure whose order is based on some combination of competence and politics. The overt values of this structure are accountability, efficiency, productivity, quality and (increasingly) cost-effectiveness. It deals primarily with tangibles, and its ultimate values, inasmuch as it is an institution, are order and predictability.

In the medical arena pastoral care discovers a model of practice that on the whole assumes professional collegiality. Its aim is the preservation and enhancement of this-worldly life and the alleviation of suffering; its skills and training are clinical and its focus is mostly pathology: that is, it is oriented to problem-solving. This model strongly emphasizes technical competence and is often highly specialized. Understandably and appropriately it is rooted in the empirical sciences and thus deals principally with aspects of reality that are tangible: observable, measurable, demonstrable, verifiable.

Note that I have described the ecclesial, institutional and medical systems in fairly traditional terms. In recent years this alignment of values and priorities has been under challenge from a society which perceives the various systems as excessively rigid, unresponsive, compartmentalized, and expensive. The effects, positive and negative, of such challenge continue to be examined in a variety of arenas.

2. Pastoral Care by Definition Deals Explicitly (Though not Exclusively) with Spiritual Aspects of Reality.

Issues of grace, sin and forgiveness, salvation, faith and transcendent meaning are the daily grist of pastoral work. Questions concerning values, ethics and morality often follow as related issues. All these, however intangible, become very tangible in pastoral care, for the circumstances of illness offer few hiding places for abstractions.

I have deliberately described the primary arena of pastoral care broadly as spirituality, because that is how I see it and that is also how I see it being perceived by increasing numbers of practitioners and clients. Issues, concerns and responses that may be more strictly defined as religious (such as ritual or sacramental practices, specific doctrinal or moral teachings, predicaments of affiliation with—or alienation from—a particular religious tradition) constitute a substantial part of this spiritual arena, but are by no means the whole of it.

On the other hand, there is no such thing as a generic chaplain. Individual pastoral practitioners come from particular religious traditions or denominations, are influenced and nurtured by them, and are also legitimized by them through some process of ordination, commissioning, and/or certification for ministry. Yet in pastoral care the chaplain deals with a clientele whose present spiritual concerns often do not fall neatly into religious or denominational categories. In responding to these concerns, the individual chaplain may find his or her views of spirituality and spiritual care broadened beyond the original denominational perspective, and sometimes even at odds with it. In my opinion, this forms the basis in truth for the widely held perception that chaplains tend to be at the edges of their respective religious denominations.

3. The Relationship Between Pastoral Care Tasks and the Time Required to Perform Them Is Not Readily Predictable by Standards of Measurement that Apply to Many Other Sorts of Tasks.

It is plain that pastoral care takes time, but this truth is not simple; for there is no tidy, systematic correlation between the amount of time spent in a given pastoral encounter and the weightiness of the situation or the effectiveness of the encounter. Granted, the time required for a large aggregate number of pastoral calls can be approximately predicted by experience and averages. But such predictions are of necessity imprecise because of the variables involved: the perceived gravity (either physical or spiritual) of the situation; the client's expectations and needs; the client's spiritual resources and readiness to mobilize them; the skill and resources of the chaplain. All this is to say that an effective and fruitful pastoral encounter may require a few moments, or it may require an hour; and there is no systematic way to predict which will be the case.

4. Pastoral Care Is Practiced in Circumstances in which Emotional and Spiritual Stresses Are Immediate and Relatively High.

The spiritual questions, concerns and values which arise as a daily part of the hospital scene are intangible, yet important. For many, under the appropriate conditions, they merit careful study, deliberate reflection and lifelong application.

Yet the circumstances of illness, hospitalization, suffering and death often conspire to deny those luxuries. Transcendent issues and values are circumscribed by the most pressing, immediate and physical concerns. This potent convergence of the ultimate and the immediate creates a unique setting for pastoral ministry: unique in its difficulties, its demands and its opportunities.

The urgency with which the client looks to the chaplain to embody the presence of God (and/or the church) is often striking and occasionally overwhelming. Paradoxes abound: to some, illness, hospitalization and crisis bring doubt and despair; to others they bring new dimensions of belief and readiness. Surrounded by constant reminders of limits and death, the chaplain bears witness to the hope of new life in the face of his or her own and others' mortality. Serving in an environment which places an appropriate premium on knowledge and competence, the chaplain is often enough called into situations where a quiet personal presence is all that is needed, or of any avail. In many encounters there is a jarring sense of haste; things that "shouldn't have to" happen in a hurry are compressed into a few minutes. These are only some of the existential factors that place physical, emotional and spiritual stress on the chaplain and others in the hospital environment.

5. Pastoral Care Is Emerging as a Distinct Professional Discipline Whose Values, Priorities and Methods Are at Present Sufficiently Articulated to Make It Possible to Differentiate Degrees of Quality in Pastoral Activities.

To put it another way, it is possible for chaplains on their own terms to describe a "good" pastoral visit. Briefly, we might say that a good pastoral visit is one in which the client's spiritual and other resources are mobilized to meet his or her needs, or progress is made toward that goal. The knowledge, attitudes and skills involved in providing such pastoral care are neither infused nor mandated; they are acquired by study, prayer, reflection and experience.

In light of the above assumptions I propose that the following principles are important for the manager of pastoral care: balance, clarity, mutuality, and creativity. The order in which they are presented is not intended to suggest priority.

1. Balance

It is essential for the manager of pastoral care to balance evenly and firmly the influences and requirements of the ecclesial, institutional and medical systems at the intersection of which pastoral care functions: that is, to be articulate in the language and values of all three systems, willing to develop and exercise an appropriate accountability to each, and firmly enough grounded to resist being co-opted by anyone. This is a matter of both expediency and professional integrity: expediency, because to be overly influenced by any one system is to lose credibility with the others; and integrity, because if pastoral care is a distinct professional discipline as assumed above, then in order to maintain its identity it must rest solidly on its bases—all of them.

Furthermore, a firm, balanced sense of the professional identity of pastoral care places the pastoral care manager and/or chaplain in a unique and opportune position to articulate and mediate the mutual critique of viewpoints and values that the ecclesial, institutional and medical systems offer one another simply by virtue of their co-existence in the health-care institution. The more solidly pastoral care rests on all its supporting systems, the greater the likelihood of its being able credibly to facilitate fruitful dialogue and critique that is prophetic rather than merely adversarial. The field of biomedical ethics is a prime example of an arena in which such authentic dialogue is beginning today.

2. *Clarity*

I see two reasons why clarity is a vital principle in the administration of pastoral services: pastoral care deals primarily with intangibles in an environment where the tangible is usually the first focus of attention; and its values, methods and skills as an emerging professional discipline are not always self-evident to its various constituencies.

Thus it is important for the administrator of pastoral services to have a clear vision of the nature of the work: its professional identity, its value and its boundaries. It is also important to articulate that vision clearly to the several constituencies which have a legitimate interest in it, but whose data and expectations may not always be germane. And, finally, it is important to promote a manner of actually providing pastoral services that is a clear expression of the values that are espoused; hence, there must be clarity of vision, of articulation and of action.

3. *Mutuality*

One of the truths that many chaplains strikingly encounter in the course of their clinical training is the principle of mutuality: the fundamental equality of all persons that transcends differences of race, gender, education, religious tradition, role or position. In pastoral care and its management, mutuality implies that:

- in chaplain-client relationships the chaplain is often in some sense the recipient as well as the giver of care;

- in administrative relationships the task and process of making decisions, organizing and performing the work are not rigidly stratified nor excessively bound by role expectations;

- in peer relationships distinctions based on gender, ordination or religious tradition are less important than a common identity as persons and professionals in ministry;

- in interdisciplinary relationships each discipline can in principle make a relevant contribution to the totality of the healing enterprise;

- in educational relationships the role distinction between teacher and learner is not always sharp, and occasionally is reversed, since learning is a lifelong process for us all.

Stating mutuality thus as a principle is not to espouse some vaguely benign egalitarianism as an excuse for lack of clarity. It is precisely within a framework of mutuality that clear and legitimate distinctions of role, function and religious tradition best find their appropriate place and value. But mutuality as I understand it is foundational as a deeply held conviction of fundamental equality, and implies the habitual inclination to implement that conviction in practical ways.

4. Creativity

Creativity is perhaps more important today in the management of pastoral services than at any time in the past. Rapid and sweeping changes in the field of health care have created an environment that is both threatening and opportune. Managers of pastoral care need to be willing to explore and expand the possibilities of working in new settings, delivering pastoral services in new ways, relating to other health care professionals in new frameworks and generally making contributions to the care of the sick that were not possible even a few years ago. On the other hand, the very survival of pastoral services as a significant part of the new health care scene also presents a challenge to the creativity of pastoral practitioners and managers: the challenge of articulating, practicing and justifying the value of pastoral care in a pluralistic and highly cost-conscious environment.

Given the above assumptions and principles, it remains to consider the specific tasks of pastoral care management. Plainly the single all-embracing responsibility of the pastoral care manager is to provide for the delivery of high-quality pastoral services to clients in a given setting. Within this overall responsibility fall several interrelated and overlapping tasks which in application are not always easy to distinguish or prioritize—as will become evident in what follows.

Nevertheless, the first priority of pastoral care management is:

1. To Define the Task in the Setting.

That is, with the hospital's leadership to reach a mutually satisfactory understanding of (a) what constitutes "high-quality pastoral care"; (b) the scope of pastoral services that the hospital wishes to make available to its clients. Such an understanding, if it is to be both valid and feasible, must be responsive to the following:

- the identity and purpose of the hospital as evidenced in statements of mission, philosophy and goals;
- the personal and professional identity of the pastoral care director and staff;
- the standards and guidelines of professional pastoral care organizations;
- the convictions of the hospital's leadership;
- the needs and sensitivities of the clientele.

If I were considering a new position as a pastoral care director, or founding a department of pastoral care "from scratch," arriving at this definition would be my first task. In fact, most of us are not in that position. Instead, we inhabit situations with certain assumptions and given factors already operative, making it more difficult to reach a clear consensus about the place of pastoral care in the hospital. Nevertheless it is important to reach such a consensus, even piecemeal and in retrospect; for lacking a satisfactory philosophical basis for pastoral care hampers subsequent administrative efforts: authority and accountability may be unclear; appropriate budget and staffing policies are difficult to determine; and the worth of pastoral services is nearly impossible to evaluate with any degree of objectivity. Conversely, to the extent that there is clear understanding and agreement about the role and priority of pastoral care in the institution, other managerial tasks become easier. Accountability can be clearly defined; planning, staffing, budgeting and evaluation all have a context within which they can receive appropriate emphasis.

The ability to carry out effectively the above task presupposes in the pastoral care manager a certain familiarity with the institutional language and values. If this familiarity is not already present, task #2 below becomes the first priority—of urgency if not importance.

2. To Learn the Language.

Coming as they do from an ecclesial base, pastoral care practitioners are presumably more or less fluent in the language and paradigms of the ecclesial system. It is not to be assumed that these are identical to the language and paradigms of the medical and institutional systems, even in religious institutions. In order to undertake other tasks effectively, the pastoral care manager must understand and appreciate the meanings and values of the medical and institutional systems. This does not mean accepting or adopting them uncritically, but understanding is a prerequisite for effective dialogue.

Assuming that (1) and (2) above are in some state of progress or resolution, the next and most obvious task of the manager of pastoral services is:

3. To Recruit, Organize and Maintain a Chaplaincy Staff to Perform Pastoral Services as Required in the Given Setting.

What follows is a series of observations pertaining to various aspects of this basic task. These observations are not presented in a rigorously systematic fashion, nor are they exhaustive by any means.

RECRUITMENT (or, alternatively, development of existing staff) implies first of all having a clear vision of what constitutes a competent chaplain. Appropriate credentials (such as professional certification) normally provide at least a minimum guarantee of pastoral training and competence. Beyond that, it is important for the manager of pastoral services to contribute his or her own perceptions and expertise to complete the picture. In my opinion, a competent chaplain should possess the following qualities:

- the faith and sensitivity to pay serious attention to the client's multi-dimensional reality—physical, psychological, social and spiritual;

- the courage and integrity to give first priority to the client's needs over those of the family, the clinicians, the church, the hospital, or the chaplain himself or herself;

- the capacity to build trust through listening, empathy and appropriate self-disclosure;

- the perceptiveness to discern and to clarify needs, resources and options;

- the willingness to empower the client rather than to foster dependency on the chaplain;

- the patience and humility to realize that not all of this is likely to be accomplished at once, nor by any one person;

- the willingness and ability to relate to a variety of others in a spirit of mutuality;

- the knowledge of self and others that makes effective use of the above qualities possible.

Having a clear vision of the "competent chaplain," the pastoral care manager needs to implement that vision by articulating it in terms sufficiently behavioral to form the basis for concrete instruments such as job descriptions and evaluations. This is admittedly not easy, but the attempt needs to be made (in consultation with the hospital's department of human resources) for the sake of an honest congruence between what is officially stated and what is really desired.

ORGANIZATION. In day-to-day administrative matters I am a professed minimalist. It has been my experience that those who gravitate into chaplaincy as a full-time professional commitment are generally persons who tend to function well in low-structure situations, and can be trusted to utilize time and resources appropriately with a minimum of supervision. In other words, I am inclined to believe in the personal integrity and professional competence of those within my sphere of management, and consequently do not feel a need to exercise a high degree of control over their daily activities.

This perception is further reflected in my belief that the best sort of management for pastoral care lies in the minimum of structure necessary to organize pastoral work effectively and still remain reasonably consistent with the rest of the hospital's administration (which includes departments whose organizational needs are more complex than those of chaplaincy). Ideally, position classifications, policies and procedures, budgets and evaluation mechanisms should all reflect this same approach.

In the day-to-day operations of pastoral care, collaboration is important. Decisions affecting the functioning of the entire pastoral team should, as much as possible, be arrived at by consensus. This is not always feasible for a variety of reasons, but I promote it as much as I can on the premise that the most relevant data about any task is supplied by those who do the work, and thus needs to be heeded in decision-making.

Finally, it is a long-standing bias of mine not to devote my time and energies exclusively to management tasks. I believe it is important—at least it is to me—to remain involved in direct patient care on an ongoing and substantial basis. Fellow chaplains respect this, and it helps me to remember that our common priority is to provide pastoral care.

NUMBERS. The issue of what constitutes an appropriate chaplain/patient ratio has been much studied, and the recommendations of professional organizations remain somewhat flexible in the neighborhood of 1/50. An appropriate level of staffing in a given instance will depend upon such factors as the nature of the facility, its case mix, acuity and patient length-of-stay. In any event, staffing should be sufficient to provide pastoral services according to established priorities, and still to leave time and energy to devote to the important task of building and maintaining healthy and harmonious working relationships among the chaplains themselves.

DEPARTMENTAL ENVIRONMENT. In my experience, even the most competent of chaplains cannot perform high-quality pastoral work over an extended period of time without the ongoing support and challenge of his or her peers. This is particularly true because of the stresses to which I alluded earlier. Thus one of the first qualities I look for in a prospective chaplain is the ability and willingness to relate to fellow chaplains in genuine personal and professional mutuality. This means trusting both the professional competence and the personal integrity and good will of one's colleagues. It does not necessarily mean cultivating intimate friendships; and it certainly does not mean "feeling good about each other" all the time. In the end, it implies replicating in the peer relationship the same qualities of trust, openness, compassion and respect that chaplains learn to value in relationships with clients. To the extent that these conditions exist in a chaplaincy department it may be truly said to be a department of pastoral care: pastoral and caring to its clients and to its members. Conversely, a department that does not form an environment of pastoral care for its own members cannot for any appreciable period of time extend pastoral care to its clients. The functions may continue, but the spirit withers, and whatever religiosity is present becomes merely a veneer to cover a lack of deep spirituality.

It is clear that the administrative leader of the department bears considerable responsibility for setting such a pastoral tone, both as "boss" and as peer. In my opinion, it is precisely in this that the pastoral identity of the director of chaplaincy resides, be that person man or woman, lay or religious, ordained or not. The challenge of performing administrative tasks (including making and enforcing unpopular policies, squeezing budgets, taking corrective or disciplinary action) in a manner that preserves the values noted above is considerable; but it is in attempting to meet that challenge that the particular identity of the administrator of pastoral services lies. Otherwise he or she becomes just another bureaucrat. This is not to suggest that other department managers should not, or do not, promote these same values; but it is absolutely vital for the pastoral care manager to do so for the sake of his or her pastoral identity and that of the department.

The above approach to pastoral care management is rooted in an incarnational spirituality: that is, it accepts as legitimate—in fact as imperative—the human agenda of imitating the divine initiative that embodies in tangible persons, objects and institutions the action and qualities of the God we cannot see. It occurs to me that such an incarnational emphasis is relevant to the "Catholic identity" of the hospital. It may be that this is the unique and characteristic contribution that Catholic institutions can make to the field of health care.

4. To Maintain Communications with the Various Constituencies to whom Pastoral Services Are a Relevant Concern.

A pastoral care department does not exist in a vacuum. Identifiable constituencies which have a legitimate interest in pastoral services are:

- the hospital structure: administration, staff, other departments, sponsoring bodies;

- professional pastoral care and other cognate organizations;

- ecclesial bodies and their officials; local parishes, pastors and staff;

- the public.

A pastoral care manager's communication responsibilities to these sometimes overlapping constituencies are a combination of accountability, advocacy and "marketing."

ACCOUNTABILITY. The accountability of pastoral care to the hospital's administrative and other structures is immediate and direct. In matters of organization, personnel and other policies, budgets, salaries, reporting and evaluation, pastoral care is part of the hospital's structure and is accountable to it. Accountability to ecclesial structures and professional organizations, though somewhat more remote, is likewise well established, particularly as it pertains to ordination, professional training, and certification for ministry.

For chaplains as well as members of other professions, public accountability is a growing phenomenon. Until recently the position of physicians, clergy and other helping professionals was assumed in the public forum to be beyond question and above reproach. Today this assumption no longer holds. Chaplains and other professionals are subject to public scrutiny (and sometimes judgment) of their practice and its results.

It is important for the pastoral care manager not to begrudge or circumvent accountability to these various constituencies, but to participate in ongoing dialogue whose goal is to adapt mechanisms of accountability to applications that respect the unique character of pastoral care and still serve their respective purposes.

ADVOCACY AND "MARKETING." The other side of accountability is advocacy. To the extent that my earlier assumption is accurate (i.e. that pastoral care is emerging as a professional discipline), then it is particularly important for the manager of pastoral services to explain, teach, clarify and generally speak for pastoral care to the constituencies noted above.

Increasingly, in fact, the pastoral care manager and/or chaplain finds himself or herself in the position of a "sales" person. Formerly it was assumed that the public value of certain services—spiritual ones among them—was established, needing no explanation or justification. In today's cost-conscious society, that is no longer true.

This has its negative side; many members of the humanitarian, service, and religious professions consider it an indignity and a waste of time to have to explain or justify their activity. I do not agree with those who consider it an indignity; there is no inherent reason why clergy, physicians, attorneys or counselors should be immune from having to demonstrate their value to society. On the other hand (at least as currently practiced) it may be a waste of time. It does not tax the imagination too far to conjure up a future in which service professionals will be spending more time documenting, explaining, justifying and selling their work than in doing the work itself.

On the positive side, the present circumstances do require those of us who practice these professions to reintegrate our ideas of what we do, to articulate them clearly, to do what we do competently, and to demonstrate its value convincingly. In this respect our cost-conscious, contentious, litigious environment does bring about the advancement of chaplaincy and other professions. The manager of pastoral services has a leadership role and responsibility in this scenario.

As I conclude this chapter I see that it has taken a philosophical tone. There is little "how-to" information about the practicalities of administering a department of pastoral care. So be it. It is certainly likely that your experience of pastoral care management will prompt reflections from your own perspective that may be similar to mine, or quite different. In either case, we are now in a position to accumulate a body of experience (perhaps even wisdom) about the organization and administration of pastoral care, and its place within the larger frameworks of health care and ecclesial ministry. I hope this paper will serve as part of that process.

Sara Carter, C.C.V.I.

Quality Assurance

The social order requires constant improvement. It must be founded in truth, built on justice and enlivened by love: it should grow in freedom toward a more human equilibrium.[1]

Catholic health care institutions seek to respond to and be in compliance with standards and criteria set forth by the various accrediting bodies. One such is: each health care institution will have a written plan and documented evidence of an ongoing quality assurance program.

Quality assurance is a descriptive title for a method by which services in a health care institution systematically and periodically conduct and document a self-evaluation of the quality of services provided for and received by the public served. The objective of this model of self-evaluation is to conduct an ongoing search for areas where quality of performance by the provider of care may be improved.

The information thus gleaned is used for educational purposes: to learn how set objectives are being met, to identify educational needs of staff, to measure the effectiveness of established policies or procedures to meet specific patient needs. Quality assurance may also be used by management to afford direction for discerning and determining the quality of services given or the need to diversify or consolidate services.

Pastoral Care Departments Need Self-Study

As a form of self-evaluation a quality assurance program is a reality in all health care institutions accredited by the Joint Commission on Accreditation of Hospitals (JCAH), and is a requirement for attaining or retaining accreditation. Review of the current literature on quality assurance indicated pastoral services, though not required by standards to do quality assurance studies, are involved in quality

79

assurance activity for pastoral care departments. In these plans and studies there is an indication that the medical model is the framework for organizing quality assurance programs on pastoral services. Actual studies tend to focus on the management dimension of pastoral services.

The Catholic Health Association published *Guidelines for Evaluating Departments of Pastoral Care*,[2] and the National Association of Catholic Chaplains[3] also offers similar guidelines. Because they are already in place, these guidelines can be used by managers of pastoral care departments as a basis for quality assurance studies of management, and plans for further development of services. However, to focus quality assurance studies exclusively on this level of ministry is to overlook the core of ministry itself. Therefore, the quality and appropriateness of pastoral service which transforms human lives and proclaims the kingdom of God is a more apt focus for quality assurance studies in pastoral ministry today. The church as sacrament calls us to be ministers in such a way as to integrate human, domestic, professional and scientific activities with religious values.[4] The Jesus of the New Testament, the Jesus of the parables, is ever promulgating the timeless truths of religion and ethics. His ethical teaching is above all a religious ethics intimately connected with the reign of God proclaimed. Jesus is always commenting on what is happening concretely in his own ministry. It is to this concreteness that the pastoral minister is also called as a follower of Jesus. As a follower of Jesus one is called to minister in the present reality while being drawn in the direction of the final stage of the kingdom of God, the vision of God.

Quality assurance in the context of pastoral services in health care is a synonym for stewardship. Stewardship calls us to reflect on the gifts of time, talent and treasure, and to determine if we are using them to extend the mission of Jesus Christ in our world. The words "steward," "good steward," and "stewardship" enjoy a permanent place in sacred scripture especially in the parables. For the most part these biblical words deal with a service or a function. The parables in particular explain that the natural function of a steward is to be responsible for the management of his master's affairs, in addition to giving an account to the master for how these affairs were administered.[5] In the context of already established guidelines for pastoral care departments, there are standards and delineation of principles which can measure the responsiveness of pastoral care management as steward. Stewardship, as already indicated, has to do with service and function. How does one approach quality assurance for the pastoral ministry encounter at the hands-on level itself?

Discipleship involves imitating the pattern of Jesus' life lived in openness to God's will and in service to others[6] in the midst of everyday occupations to people of every age, in the workplace as well as in the marketplace. The quality assurance plans for pastoral services might more sharply focus on the quality of the pastoral encounter in the context of discipleship. The pastoral minister as disciple finds identity with Jesus Christ and his message. This, then, is the primary focus for monitoring the appropriateness of pastoral care given and the outcome achieved. Because it is not too concrete, the quality of ministry as expressed in Christian discipleship is less accessible for evaluation by established models of quality assurance. Yet it is uniquely in the area of discipleship that one will find the embodiment of the very nature of pastoral care in our health care institutions. Pastoral care is being identified as the service which is most apt to witness to the mission of the Catholic institution as church, wherein is made known the true and profoundly Christian meaning of the dignity of the human person and the sacredness of human life. *Gaudium et Spes* offers an example of a standard for the pastoral ministry encounter: to harmonize with the authentic interests of human persons, in accordance with God's will and design, and to enable each person as an individual and as a member of society to pursue and fulfill his or her total vocation.[7] In a unique way the pastoral person's relationship with God is intimately bound up with his or her relationship to the other person in the act of ministering. The other person is an equal, not only in frailty and powerlessness before God but also in his or her rights and dignity. Value resides in the person because his or her life and existence are a gift from God.

The gospels narrate the necessity for Jesus as God's anointed to call people to conversion, to proclaim the kingdom of God in his teaching, and to enact it in his ministry. Jesus called his disciples to follow him and to share in his ministry. They are to be the nucleus of that community which will continue the activity of proclaiming and building God's kingdom through the centuries. Matthew presents Jesus commissioning them specifically to make disciples of all nations, baptizing them and teaching them to observe all that he had taught them. It is because Jesus called his disciples to share his ministry that the pastoral minister today looks at the quality of his or her own discipleship.

Aspects To Be Evaluated

In quality assurance terms, the questions may be: To what extent does the minister imitate the love of Jesus? How does he or she transform human lives? How does the minister form a community built on respect for human dignity, solidarity and justice, so that the community is a sign of the power and presence of God? In 2 Corinthians Paul appeals for reconciliation in Christ because the community status as "the new creation" is not an assumed possession but something that is constantly worked out.[8] The questions which will evaluate the ongoing working out of the community as new creation, God's saving act in Christ and the ongoing work of apostolic ministry are not asked separately. The second is an extension of the first, part of the same salvation history. The tendency to dichotomize between the faith professed and the practice of faith crises in daily life (professional and social activity on the one hand and religious life on the other) are brought into dialogue by the pastoral minister in the pastoral encounter.

Patients who seek pastoral care trust the judgment, know-how and confidentiality engaged in the pastoral encounter. When they are seeking pastoral answers, patients are also saying that they are placing themselves into a value system of a tradition and communion which they consider relevant. They are asking for their issues to be placed in a pastoral perspective. The question arises: How does the minister respond to the patient criteria for ministry?

Paul Pruyser in *The Minister as Diagnostician* identifies the pastoral triage situation in which the minister makes a diagnosis.[9] The same author asks the question: How does the minister proceed to heal, guide and sustain the person who turns to him or her for assistance? This is an apt question to both evaluate and offer ministry to the people of God. Patients turn to pastoral care services for reasons they explicitly connect with faith, with a spirit of prayer and trust in the presence of the spirit of God. In addition, within the Roman Catholic institution this connection with faith extends to the Christian sacraments and sacramental life. The consciousness of the pastoral minister extends to who he or she is as church with intentional integration of the healing ministry into the very present moment of ministry. The minister reveals and discloses in his or her ministry the gospel vision of peace and justice as a way of life, witnessing to the Lord and his message by knowing it, preaching it and using it creatively.

The following are offered as some touchstones for evaluation of the proclamation of the kingdom by pastoral care services in the health care ministry. Each Catholic institution's pastoral care staff has the responsibility for the quality of services which articulates and is in dialogue with the Christian mission of the sponsoring institution.

- Upholding the gospel values of the sacredness of life and the dignity of the human person.

- Communicating the message of the gospel of Jesus' call to his followers to live a life in unison with the Father as well as in positive loving relationship with others.

- Relating to the specific charism and mission of the institution with its expressed or implicit service and responsibility.

- Making known the true and profoundly religious meaning of reconciliation and its full scope of influence.

- Facilitating conversion which bears fruit in the person's life to include acts of reconciliation which pass unobserved in their daily ordinariness, overcoming conflicts and restoring unity.

- Proclaiming to all the truth that saves.

- Promoting social justice which is constitutive to religious life and living, acknowledging the basic equality between all people.

- Educating persons to the quality of social and moral virtues and assisting them to take part in decisions for their own lives as a right in freedom.

- Creating a climate and environment which is hospitable toward and invitational in fact to communal celebration in worship: sacrament, liturgy and paraliturgy.

Pastoral care is in a unique position to witness to the ecclesial dimension of the presence and function of the church in health care. This witness is precisely visible where ecclesiology and technology intersect. It is this intersecting that is the cutting edge of self-evaluation of pastoral care: the meaning of suffering which always remains a mystery, and technological progress which may help supply material for human advancement but is powerless to actualize it.[10]

In more concrete terms the nature of self-evaluation of pastoral services as identified in the context of this chapter reveals the quality of pastoral presence. In preference to using volume of activity indicated primarily by numbers, evaluation might be more appropriately reflected as density of pastoral time and outcomes. The density of a pastoral visit may be described in terms of a quality, in that a visit may be qualitatively supportive, pastoral, sacramental or social in nature. A supportive visit stresses the person's psychological well-being and addresses internal tensions such as anxiety, self-acceptance, and interpersonal conflicts. In a pastoral visit there is a religious existential approach to the whole person in a relationship with God. The sacramental visit denotes the Christian experience of God as a personal encounter, wherein the encounter of God and the human person is sealed symbolically. A social visit occurs when the pastoral person visits the patient on a social basis stressing the social well-being of the patient and the pastoral person. In extending ministry to the patient's family, to hospital staff and to physicians, identical qualities apply. Harshajan's *Counseling and Health Care* is helpful in developing criteria for quality of pastoral ministry encounters.[11]

Responses to the Results of the Evaluation

Looking at outcomes from the pastoral ministry encounter, the pastoral services may want to evaluate, for example, the shift in practice of cardiopulmonary resuscitation because the meaning of the dignity of the person and sacredness of life is actualized by pastoral staff and understood by patient family, staff and physicians. This same can apply to time spent on patient care team conferences, pastoral consultation, and multidisciplinary staff conferences. The time spent in these activities can be recorded. A consultation report of the percentage of time spent in the various pastoral ministry encounters can serve as an evaluative tool to show focus of service: patient visits, team conferences, family ministry, staff meetings. This can also allow for shift of focus if needed. All recorded activity and time spent is established by the individual pastoral staff member, so reports are what the pastoral person says of himself or herself. Should the institution have computer services, accumulation of data for quality assurance studies by computer has many possibilities. This approach could satisfy the requirement to obtain data for study while at the same time keeping time spent on documentation at a minimum level. The format for generating pastoral information for self-evaluation and follow-up action is of necessity specific to each institution. Data gathering, type and volume is to some extent shaped by the method of accumulating the data whether it is done manually or with computer assistance. Presuming that computer assistance is available, all basic patient information is available and can be expanded to the desired program limits on a daily basis.

A computer program designed to accumulate data for quality assurance of direct hands-on ministry would include some key indicators. Each can be defined and converted to a specific code symbol, as the table ahead indicates.

I. Patient Visits
  1. Type: initial, follow-up, family, hospital staff, medical staff, on-call or pre-operative visits. Each type of visit would need its own code.
  2. Quality: supportive, pastoral, sacramental, social. Each visit would have one of these four qualities assigned it.
  3. Time spent.
II. Meetings
  1. Type: multidisciplinary team conference, patient care team conference, staff support, patient support, family support, etc.
  2. Time spent.
III. Prayer Services
  1. Ecumenical, memorial, daily eucharistic liturgy, etc.
  2. Time spent.
IV. Department Activities
  1. Employee orientation, in-service education, management, clinical pastoral education, etc.
  2. Time spent.
V. Community Activities
  1. Parish presentation, clergy meeting, volunteer education, funerals, etc.
  2. Time spent.
VI. Other Areas of Ministry
  1. On-call time, emergency room ministry, radiation therapy, hemodialysis, same day surgery.
  2. Time given in block time.

As a method of personal accountability the chaplain reflects the kind of patient visits made, the length of time involved for each visit, as well as all other pastoral services rendered during duty time. The updated report can be entered into the computer daily, generating an updated report for the following day. The cumulative monthly

The computer can be very effectively programmed to capture information which is used for quality assurance studies for pastoral care. The activity of the pastoral department for each institution is defined by that institution's goals and objectives for patient service. Any program for quality assurance will be designed to articulate with the goals and objectives of the institution. One method of accumulating data for a quality assurance study will include identity of: persons served, the quality of the pastoral encounter and the length of time spent in the encounter. The following sample might serve as a construct for accumulation of data. The definition of activity and the quality desired has to be tailored to the unique needs of each pastoral care service.

BASIC INFORMATION

Rm.	Patient	Activity	Quality	Length	Chaplain	Rel.	Age	Adm.
203	Jane Heart	Initial visit	Supportive	$\frac{1}{2}$ hour	SC	C	80	3/29/89
204	John Doe	Follow-up	Sacramental	15 min.	SC	C	65	3/26/89
205	Maria Inez	Family	Pastoral	1 hour	SC	P	34	3/18/89
		Meeting		2 hours				
		Liturgy		45 min.				
		E.R.		$3\frac{1}{2}$ hrs				
			Total:	8 hours				

Converted to computer language the report would read as follows:

		ACT.	QAL	LNTH	V.S.
203	Jane Heart	100	200	030	S
204	John Doe	105	210	015	S
205	Maria Inez	110	205	060	S
		300		120	
		430		045	
		965		210	
			Total:	480	

The computer can convert these figures to hours and percentages according to the activity and time given. A monthly report can be obtained which gives the total time spent in hours and in percentage by each chaplain reflecting varied activities. A by-product of this is that a combined report of the activity of each chaplain reflects the percentage of time spent by the department as a whole in the various activities. These monthly reports and the totals for the annual report can be used to measure the effectiveness of established policies, the quality of service given, and the percentage of time spent in specific activities which can be measured by stated objectives. The individual report can be a source of evaluation of performance, and for budgeting purposes as well.

report then offers a base for information of activity, the extent to which pastoral ministry is meeting established annual objectives, whether the policies of the department are followed, and the quality of ministry practiced.

Pastoral ministry derives its perspective from a Christian faith commitment. The point of convergence for Christian life in Christian morality must be the reality of God as he reveals himself in Jesus Christ. The quality assurance program for pastoral care, focusing on the chaplain, will always create a tension of uneasiness. It invites the chaplain to an open-ended vulnerability and insecurity, as well as to an increased awareness for the need to minister together with others for continued growth in freedom for the human person. Collaboration occurs in an atmosphere of faith, in a spirit of prayer and with the guidance of the Holy Spirit.

Notes

1. Pope John XXIII, *Pacem in Terris*, 55.
2. Catholic Health Association, Guidelines for Evaluating Departments of Pastoral Care, 1984.
3. National Association of Catholic Chaplains, Printed Guidelines.
4. Austin P. Flannery, editor, *Documents of Vatican II*, "Gaudium et Spes," 43.
5. Alexander Jones, editor, *The Jerusalem Bible*, Matthew 25:14–30.
6. United States Catholic Conference, "Pastoral Letter on Catholic Sacred Teaching and the United States Economy," Chapter II, #4.
7. "Gaudium et Spes," 35.
8. *The Jerusalem Bible*, 2 Corinthians 5:16–6:2.
9. Paul Pruyser, *The Minister as Diagnostician*, 1976, p. 45.
10. "Gaudium et Spes," 35.
11. Pazhayatil Harshajan, *Counseling and Health Care*, 1977, pp. 49–66.

Rodger F. Accardi

Rehabilitation:
Dreams Lost, Dreams Found

Case I: George is a fifty-seven year old salesman. His wife found him collapsed on the floor of the basement work room. Paramedics rushed him to the nearest emergency room. They diagnosed the problem as a severe stroke and admitted him to the intensive care unit. Though the family thought he would not survive, after two weeks, the acute medical problems stabilized and he was discharged to the rehabilitation unit. He is paralyzed on one side of his body; though he cannot produce any speech, his cognitive abilities are relatively intact.

Case II: June is a forty-two year old housewife, mother of three adolescents. While weekend shopping with her husband, she suddenly experienced weakness in her legs. Within hours she could not walk at all. After two weeks of tests at the local general hospital, she appeared to have multiple sclerosis and was transferred to the local rehabilitation center for treatment.

Case III: Shirley, thirty-two, injured her back at the assembly line four years ago. She has had several back surgeries since then, and her pain has worsened. She is unemployed, separated from her husband, and has two small children. She was admitted to the rehabilitation hospital with a diagnosis of low back pain.

Case IV: Joe is a twenty-eight year old employee at a local fast food restaurant. He is married with one young child. During a swim party at a neighbor's house, he had a freak diving accident. Tests indicate that his spinal cord is severed and that he is paralyzed from the waist down.

Each of the four cases above is unique. Yet they are all typical characterizations of patients admitted to a rehabilitation unit or hospital. The average length of in-patient stay is thirty days. Most patients are referred from the general hospital after the acute medical crisis has stabilized.

Most patients arrive at the rehabilitation unit with an implicit model of health that is quickly challenged. They believe that illness exists because of an invasion of disease, and that when the cure is administered and the disease removed, health will be restored. The disabled person begins to realize that there are no cures on the road to health, that total physical restoration is not possible. What does it mean, then, for a spinal cord injured patient to be "ill" at admission, and be considered "well," yet still spinal cord injured, at discharge? While achieving maximum functional outcomes and abilities is a common rehabilitation goal, what do wellness and health mean to the disabled? Rehabilitation, the task of rebuilding one's very life, includes the psychological adjustment to disability and the spiritual process of transformation.

A common sequence of emotional changes in the rehabilitation process consists of acute disorganization, assessment, mourning and re-entry. When George is first admitted with the diagnosis of stroke, he is shocked and exhibits powerful, disorganized emotions. He cannot believe the diagnosis and its implications and he begins to question why this crisis has happened to him.

June begins the assessment phase by seeking accurate information regarding her multiple sclerosis. She begins to recognize the physical, intellectual and emotional changes in her functioning. Her moods fluctuate between anger, depression, wishful thinking and self-disgust. She has begun to find answers to why this has happened, but is not quite ready to plan for the future.

Shirley has entered the process of mourning the multiple losses in her life due to or compounded by her chronic pain. She moves in and out of therapeutic depression with each recognition of loss. She is involved in re-evaluating her attachments and detachments. She is very engaged in the rehabilitation program while beginning to make plans for the many changes in her family, social and vocational life.

Joe is nearly ready for discharge and re-entry back to an active life. His home has been adapted to meet his special needs. He has made application to and been accepted at a school to complete his degree in business administration. He has been in dialogue with his former employer about the possibility of managing within the chain of restaurants. Joe and his wife are talking about expanding their family by pursuing adoption procedures.

Adjustment to disability seldom occurs in the mannerly flow depicted here. Rather, there is fluid movement between these stages related to the beneficial effects of the rehabilitation program and the pre-morbid personality dynamics of the individual.

Each disabled individual experiences significant loss. For some, it is the loss of a body part through amputation. For others, it is a loss of bodily function, for example, walking, bowel/bladder functioning, or sexual functioning. Many experience the loss of identity, meaning, hopes and expectations.

These losses point to the loss of a dream, a dream that may have sustained one's world until the time of disability. This dream takes many forms: for instance, the dream of blissful retirement, the dream of being the central breadwinner, the dream of walking my daughter down the aisle, the dream of raising a large family, the dream of what it means to be a man-husband-father, to be a woman-wife-mother.

The process of mourning for the disabled individual is similar to the separation anxiety experienced shortly after bonding occurs between newborn infant and mother. The major goal of healthy mourning is the withdrawal of emotional attachment from the lost object in order to develop new relationships. Unhealthy mourning is often described as the creation of the illusion that the lost object is really retained, thereby fortifying the denial or defense. As one realizes that total physical restoration is not possible, one's world often collapses: the disabled individual is confronted with the void, with emptiness, separation, absence.

The spiritual process of transformation is based on the belief that God dwells beyond the void. Transformation, or the movement from lower to higher orders of life, occurs throughout the life cycle along a continuous line of intention or development. Transformation is initiated by a wholly imminent and transcendent God. When the disabled individual begins to discover the God who lives beyond the void, new meaning and new dreams emerge.

Pastoral Tasks

What are some of the pastoral tasks involved in ministry with the disabled? The first task is eliciting and listening to the spiritually significant stories of the patient. Spiritually significant stories are seldom told in religious language. The common everyday stories of patients often reflect deep meaning and imply powerful impact on the patient's life. These stories may point to experiences of mystery, conversion, deliverance, blessing or curse, though that is seldom apparent to the patient. The effect of receiving the story of the other is to establish rapport. Accompanying the individual in this seemingly foreign and unsafe land of disability creates an atmosphere of security.

The next task is to indwell the story. This means entering the pain and terror of the disabled individual. Compassion is an ability to suffer with another. Therefore, indwelling also means that the chaplain must be attentive to personal dynamics of resistance and defense, so as not to confuse personal dynamics with those of the other. From within the experience of loss, the chaplain can scan the terrain and bring light to the dark areas of the cave, dungeon or pit.

The third task is that of linking the stories. One way linking can take place is in developing and nurturing support groups for patients of similar diagnoses or similar age. Many disabled individuals in the early stages of rehabilitation begin to fixate on their loss. Coming together with people who have similar stories, but who may be further along in the journey of adjustment to disability, can effect personal transformation. One of the greatest privileges we as ministers enjoy is not only linking individual stories together, but then weaving these stories with the stories of God. These stories of deliverance, reconciliation, redemption and salvation reside in scripture, in the tradition of a people, and in the inner life of the individual. Linking can fan the flames of inner life, enabling the disabled to generate and proclaim their own bold, creative, transcending and transforming stories.

Theological Perspectives

A theological reflection on this movement of dreams being lost and dreams found for disabled persons is the story of the two men on the road to Emmaus. The recent events in Jerusalem have destroyed the dreams of the two travelers. They come upon the stranger who seems to know nothing of the death of their hero. The stranger elicits the story of their loss and establishes rapport. While they must know that the times and the roads are not safe, they feel secure in the other and share their story of disillusionment. The stranger indwells the story and begins to scan the scriptures in order to bring light to their confusion and fears.

In the linking of their personal stories with the stories of God and with the act of the breaking of the bread, the stranger becomes transparent and the travelers are transformed. Though the loss continues to be realized, a new dream emerges. A new energy is released to reorganize the personality and the world that has collapsed. The original loss is now reinterpreted in the light of the new insight which serves to free the travelers from the original conflict. There is a release of energy which drives the travelers back to Jerusalem to tell the story of the dream lost and dream found.

Lucien A. Sawyer, O.M.I.

Mental Health

The entire pastoral care movement must acknowledge its indebtedness to the mental health ministry and the pioneering efforts of Anton T. Boisen. In 1924, at Worcester State Hospital, he adapted for the training of the clergy a method used at the time in Boston for the training of young physicians. Clinical pastoral education has come a long way in sixty years, though its roots remain in the treatment of mental patients.[1]

As a result of Boisen's early accomplishments the chaplain is accepted as a peer today in most large psychiatric hospitals. Pastoral care is welcomed as part of the treatment team modality, and if the chaplain is properly qualified his or her input will be unique, respected and utilized in the treatment plan. This presentation will consider the opportunities, cautions, requirements and coming changes that affect ministry in a mental health setting, based on this writer's experience.

Chaplain as Team Member

The psychologist Paul Pruyser has given us a classical description of the effective treatment team. His point is that only a multiplicity of organized disciplines is fit to do justice to human suffering, which is always multifaceted.[2] The team must be an organic whole responding to the felt needs of the patient. The chaplain has a particular way of listening. His or her insights are as valid as the perspectives of the other disciplines, and are to be shared for the benefit of the patient.

The opportunity to share implies the responsibility for preparing an objective religious evaluation of an assigned patient and a presentation of that evaluation in a form that is acceptable to the team. Carroll Wise has suggested many areas to be covered in an essay-type religious evaluation for psychotherapy.[3] More recently, Wayne

Oates has drawn up a scale of continuums that are helpful for this task.[4] A typical summary form which may be added to the patient's medical record is described in the *AMHC Forum.*[5]

The chaplain also has many opportunities to reach and help the patient through worship. A mass or prayer service creates an atmosphere of reverence which can be more therapeutic than the words of the homily. When patients participate by singing, reading the scriptures, responding to a dialogue homily, or walking in the offertory procession, they develop a greatly needed sense of belonging. The handshake of peace becomes particularly meaningful as a gesture of reconciliation with each other, and with any staff member who may be in attendance. The communion service affords a familiar experience to patients who are otherwise overwhelmed by the threatening environment of the hospital.

The ritual for the anointing of the sick may be administered to the mentally ill at appropriate times, utilizing prayer and physical touch as a step toward healing.[6] The sacrament of reconciliation should be used with a certain discretion, preferably as discharge time approaches. At other times patients may intend to use the sacrament, which calls for absolute confidentiality, as a way of silencing the priest when they know that he is part of the treatment team. Open communication with the patient prior to treatment team meetings seems to be the most equitable stance to take.

Cautions

Although the opportunities for the chaplain are many in a mental health institution, certain cautions are in order.

Because of his or her unique and privileged position in the eyes of many patients, the chaplain may tend to be a loner in the hospital. This is especially true when the treatment team approach seems to be floundering. Unless he or she takes the initiative and approaches other therapists the chaplain's insight may not always be sought. The chaplain owes it to the patients, as well as to the staff, to make his or her pastoral perspective available for a better integrated treatment plan. Much can be learned from friendly cooperation with other team members.

Next, the chaplain must not consider his or her function as exclusively that of a psychotherapist. Ministry with this attitude will inevitably prove frustrating, because complete successes are few. The chaplain's uniqueness is that in counseling he or she can draw upon the religious resources of the patient. If prayer is part of the therapy and is used honestly it is a valid spiritual experience for the patient even though the illness remains.

As the chaplain develops personal skills, he should respect the activities of the other disciplines, participate in them if appropriate, and learn from them, but never use them as a substitute for his or her own. In the eyes of the patients and staff, the chaplain represents the reality of life values. Genuine prayer must not degenerate to the level of a therapeutic technique.

Basic Requirements

Not everyone can be an effective mental health chaplain. It might be helpful at this point to consider some of the personal qualifications for this position.

First of all, the chaplain needs a clear sense of his or her personal identity as a minister. Awareness of strengths and limitations is a must. This is very difficult to achieve experientially without some form of clinical training and constant updating. Certification by a national association of professionals is indispensable for the affirmation of the chaplain as well as for the assurance of the hiring institution. Three main certifying bodies exist, whose requirements are actually quite similar. The first is the *Association of Mental Health Clergy,* which provides recognition for its members who have successfully appeared before the national certification commission and met all the requirements. It is open to clergy of all faith groups who minister to the mentally ill.[7] A second body is the *National Association of Catholic Chaplains* which grants an advanced level certification as mental health chaplain.[8] Another is the *College of Chaplains of the American Protestant Health Association.*[9] There are advantages to belonging to the first and a choice of the other two.

The chaplain has to be familiar with the structure and categories of the *DSM-III-R*[10] in order to have some handle on the patient's problem, and to understand the insight of the other therapists. But this knowledge must supplement a deep respect for the patient who is being helped, a respect that is able to put up with disappointments, deceptions, and reversals. Unless a deep commitment is present the chaplain will be perceived by the patients and staff as another functionary.

Trends

Two major trends are emerging in relation to the future of mental health treatment, and both are significantly affecting the chaplaincy.

The first is the diversification of treatment facilities. Clark Aist calls our attention to this problem and its impact upon chaplains.[11] Mental patients are no longer being treated predominantly in large mental hospitals. There are now approximately eight hundred community health centers throughout the country. Only fifteen percent of these centers include professionally trained clergy as members of their staff. Also, psychiatric units of general hospitals have become one of the largest single sources of in-patient mental health services today.[12] Finally, there is a large and growing number of private psychiatric facilities providing insurance-covered short term care. The large state hospitals, where most chaplains minister, are becoming the refuge of those who cannot afford private hospitals or whose long-term care cannot be provided elsewhere.

Since many of these general hospitals and private facilities rely upon area clergy for limited and perhaps contractual pastoral care the burden is now being placed upon trained mental health clergy to reach out to their fellow ministers in the community and provide adequate training programs. Community education will be making more demands on their time.

The second major trend in mental health treatment is far more disquieting. As a result of political and legal pressure patients are being deinstitutionalized in large numbers, without the provision of proper community support. The homeless mentally ill have created a crisis in all our American cities. The American Psychiatric Association is grappling with this reality.[13] The relative security of the institution and the treatment teams will have to be sacrificed in favor of outreaches into community agencies. An important responsibility for the chaplain must now be to look toward local churches and civic clubs for systems that can be utilized to shelter and feed the homeless.[14] The chaplain will have to address church groups of all persuasions and extend his or her support and ministry to the countless mentally ill who are vulnerable outside the protection of the institutional setting.

Even at the present time the highly specialized responsibility of the mental health chaplaincy rests on a person torn between patients in the institution requiring pastoral expertise and the greater need of those bewildered individuals in the vast outer community who more than ever need a sense of God's presence in their lives. There is no clear answer to the current struggle. Chaplains as a group must now explore innovative ways to address the problems of the future as creatively as they have met those of the past.

Notes

1. S. Hiltner, "The Debt of Clinical Pastoral Education to Anton D. Boisen," *Journal of Pastoral Care,* 1966, Vol. 20, No. 3, pp. 129–135.

2. P. W. Pruyser, "Religion in the Psychiatric Hospital: A Reassessment," *Journal of Pastoral Care,* 1984, Vol. 38, No. 1, pp. 6–7.

3. C. A. Wise, *Pastoral Psychotherapy* (New York: Jacob Aronson Inc., 1980), Chapters 4 and 5.

4. W. E. Oates, "Some Functions of Belief in Illness and Health," *Cura Animarum* (published by the Association of Mental Health Clergy and formerly known as *AMHC Forum*), 1985, Vol. 37, No. 1, p. 11.

5. L. A. Sawyer, "A Pastoral Assessment for the Psychiatric Team in the Age of *DSM-3*," *AMHC Forum,* 1981, Vol. 34, No. 1, pp. 8–12.

6. *Pastoral Care of the Sick,* approved by the National Council of Catholic Bishops (New York: Catholic Book Publishing Co., 1983), p. 39, no. 53.

7. *The Association of Mental Health Clergy,* Rev. George E. Doebler, Executive Director, 12320 River Oaks Point, Knoxville, TN 37922.

8. *The National Association of Catholic Chaplains,* 3501 So. Lake Drive, Milwaukee, WI 53207–0473.

9. *The College of Chaplains of the American Protestant Health Association,* 1701 East Woodfield Road, Suite 311, Schaumburg, IL 60195.

10. *Diagnostic and Statistical Manual of Mental Disorders—Revised* (Washington, DC: American Psychiatric Association, 1987).

11. C. S. Aist, "The New Shape of Mental Health Ministry," *Cura Animarum,* 1984, Vol. 36, No. 1, p. 21.

12. M. J. Witkin, "Trends in Patient Care Episodes in Mental Health Facilities, 1955–77," *Mental Health Statistical Note* No. 154 (Rockville, MD: National Institute of Mental Health, 1980), p. 12.

13. R. Lamb, M. D., ed. *The Homeless Mentally Ill* (Washington, DC: American Psychiatric Association, 1984).

14. R. D. Anderson, Jr. "Deinstitutionalization: Mental Health and Religious Communities," *AMHC Forum,* 1979, Vol. 32, No. 2, pp. 53–56.

Teresa Maltby, R.S.M.

Pastoral Care of the Aging

Anna Mae was in her mid-eighties when she developed gangrene in her foot and was informed she would have to have her leg amputated or she would die. Anna Mae steadfastly refused the operation. Her physician and the nursing staff were very distressed by her refusal because they thought she would tolerate the surgery quite well and very likely live several more years. They pleaded with the chaplain to talk to her, that is, to change her mind. Through many conversations over several days the chaplain came to know a well-integrated and prayerful woman who had lived a full and satisfying life. Fully aware of the implications of her decision not to have surgery, she actively chose to die with her body intact. The decision was made prayerfully, and Anna Mae expressed it firmly and peacefully. Over the course of their visits Anna Mae shared with the chaplain her vision of the meaning of life and death, and the chaplain came to focus her energy more on assisting the clinical staff in their struggle to understand Anna Mae's decision.

The story of Anna Mae points to several of the key issues in an effective pastoral care of the aging. The pastoral minister caring for the aging must have at least a basic understanding of the specific developmental tasks of aging, and he or she must be comfortable in the presence of irreversible diminishment and death. The inevitability of the aging process confronts the minister with his or her own mortality even without the presence of a catastrophic illness, but simply as a condition of being human. Further, the cultural resistance to aging and death challenges the minister to actively work to create a community in which aging, death and life in the face of death have meaning. As Browning has effectively argued, "Before the church can care for or counsel the aging and the aged, it must have a fund of meanings that will enable its people and the society to understand the place of aging in life; it must have a practical theology of aging."[1]

The pastoral minister can play a significant role in the development of the community's vision by bringing together the resources of the Christian tradition and the realities of the experience of aging. The resulting practical theology should challenge the presuppositions that underlie the prevailing cultural view of aging and death. This challenge, however, must include an alternative view that honestly recognizes the negatives of the aging process while at the same time focusing on the potential for significance and growth within the very experience of diminishment. The task is to articulate a context within which aging persons can make sense out of their experiences without explaining them away with the language of a soft and pseudo-faith.

One attempt at a systematic reflection on the experience of old age and death from a faith perspective is found in the work of Charles Curran.[2] Curran argues for a transformationist understanding of death, rooted in the dying and rising of the Lord, which also sheds light on the meaning of life. The five basic Christian symbols of creation, sin, incarnation, redemption and resurrection sum up the meaning of human experience. Within the symbols we can identify three aspects of death. First, biological death is a natural event and part of our reality as created beings. Second, both the Hebrew and the Christian scriptures connect death with sin. Genesis establishes the connection, and Paul reminds us that death came into the world through sin (Rom 5:12). Jesus, God incarnate, redeemed humanity by succumbing to the powers of sin and darkness in death. Third, this very death was the pre-condition for the triumph of the powers of life in the resurrection. The same reality which appeared to be the triumph of sin was transformed into the triumph of life. A practical theology of aging must incorporate all of these symbols or it is incomplete and will be untrue to experience.

The liturgical primacy of the resurrection image must not overshadow death's connection with sin. Loneliness, isolation, and loss are appropriately associated with dying, and death is an event we cannot control. The aged know facing death is painful. The chaplain knows facing death is painful. A theological vision which does not articulate and give meaning to the harsh reality of death will not be helpful to the elderly because it will not be true to their experience. The pastoral care-giver's challenge is to be so firmly alive in the resurrection that she or he can, over and over again, walk to the brink of death with those who will go through death.

A transformationist vision of death proposes more than life after death; it suggests the paschal mystery of Jesus as the paradigmatic event of all Christian experience. Through baptism Christians participate in the death-resurrection of the Lord and begin to share the first-fruits of redemption already in this life. For the baptized Christian, then, death is not the passage to a totally new life, but, rather, it is the transformation of life in this world into the fullness of life in the risen Lord. In a similar manner, all the losses and deaths of a lifetime can be seen as passages which transform one period of life into another. Death is a crisis situation not totally unlike the other crises we encounter in life. Developmental theorists and our own experiences demonstrate that growth is dependent upon dying to some portion of the past and present, and that it is inevitably painful. Within this context the losses and opportunities for growth that characterize the later years take on new meaning. The experience of aging in a person like Anna Mae illustrates this transformation in progress. As her physical powers declined, Anna Mae deepened her relationships with herself, with others, and with God. Her entire life derived meaning from her growing relationship with God. While she continued to be open to relationships with others, she was at one with herself and ultimately chose her relationship with God over all others. If those caring for the aged—family, clinicians, and pastoral care-givers—shared this perspective, the specifics of treatment plans as well as day-to-day personal interactions would reveal a respect for the aging and dying process rooted in a reverence for the dignity and uniqueness of each individual person and his or her journey.

The unique character of each one's personal journey becomes more evident in the middle and later years as age and physical development are less determinative of one's stage of growth, and environmental factors such as family and job take on more significance. The complexity of emotional development in the last half of life presents a twofold challenge to pastoral care. First, it is necessary to have at least a basic understanding of the emotional issues of the later years. Beyond understanding, however, is the necessity of accepting these issues as the minister's own. They are the care-giver's own, not only because she or he shares the human process of aging, but also because much of the work of later years begins in what Clements calls the "silent crises" of the mid-years.[3] Just as the pastoral care-giver needs to have a practical theology of aging in order to nurture a context that finds meaning in diminishment and death, so, too, must the chaplain exhibit a willingness to substitute wisdom for physique, to shift emotional investment from one person or activity to another, and to approach the new or unknown with openness and flexibility. All of these processes are essential to healthy and successful aging, and all are rooted in the responses made in the middle years.

Even the healthy and successfully aging person experiences significant physical, mental and emotional crisis. One of the better resources for understanding the nature and problems of old age is *Aging and Mental Health: Positive Psychosocial and Biomedical Approaches* by Robert Butler and Myrna Lewis. While unique personalities produce individual ways of being old, some general characteristics are fairly uniformly common to the aging population. Bodily changes offer indisputable evidence of aging. Graying and loss of hair, loss of teeth, wrinkling of skin, impaired vision and hearing and changes in posture are common signs of getting old and have implications for pastoral care. A person with decreased appetite and lessened ability to taste, especially salt and sugar, has ample reason to find a sodium-restricted diet not worth the trouble. Hearing loss is often accompanied by difficulty in organizing incoming stimuli. More often than not the pastoral care-giver having difficulty communicating with a hearing-impaired patient needs to slow down rather than talk louder. The challenge of physical decline is to befriend the body as it is and as it is becoming. A person preoccupied with his or her many illnesses needs to be helped to move beyond the physical to find a sense of identity and worth in relationships and in intellectual, artistic and spiritual pursuits.

Social and economic forces impact the lives of the elderly directly and indirectly. Retirement policies put many out of work against their will, incomes are usually significantly reduced, and the mobile family system leaves many isolated. The energy needed just to locate and take advantage of available economic and social assistance is beyond the resources of many elderly. The intricate interplay of physical, emotional and social factors needs to be considered in any health care response to sick elderly. For example, a person who is malnourished and appears disoriented may simply have neglected to eat because she was socially lonely. An effective pastoral response in such situations will likely involve the insights of several members of a multidisciplinary team.

Physical decline and diminished social and economic resources make loss a predominant characteristic of the emotional experiences of older people. Older persons expend enormous amounts of energy grieving over losses, adapting to the changes that result from loss and coping with the stress inherent in these processes. Losses of health, family, status, and adequate living resources are compounded by cultural devaluation and neglect. Loss of independence and personal dignity are more devastating the more subtle the expression. For example, a patient in a health care facility may deal much better with being incontinent than with persons talking to her as if she were a

child. Care-givers need to be particularly careful not to confuse physical dependence with lack of maturity.

Pastoral care personnel may be tempted to try to help, to make it
easier or less painful. Before assisting an older person it is wise to
reflect on what the help will mean to the one receiving it. Unsolicited
assistance may be interpreted as an indication the person is incapable
of accomplishing the task and may be an affront to his or her sense
of worth.

Treatment decisions is an area where the elderly frequently experience a loss of control. Not being allowed to direct the plan of care
according to their wishes is only one aspect of the issue. Often, the
assumption is made that he or she wouldn't be able to understand, or
the explanation may be given too quickly for an older person to
comprehend easily. What is only a need for slower communication
appears as disorientation or inability to understand. A pastoral minister may be able to facilitate the communication process and thus
enable the person to retain control over his or her care and, in so
doing, make the critical decisions that reflect his or her understanding of the meaning of life, sickness and death.

The gradual development of a sense of fulfillment and meaning
in life as life moves toward death is a result of overcoming loss,
resolving personal conflicts and deepening relationships with self,
others, and God. The resolution of life's experiences and problems is
facilitated through a normal life review process. Life review "is characterized by the progressive return to consciousness of past experiences and particularly the resurgence of unresolved conflicts that can
be looked at again and reintegrated. If the integration is successful, it
can give new significance and meaning to one's life and prepare one
for death, by mitigating fear and anxiety."[4] Life review may occur in
mild forms of story-telling and reminiscence sometimes accompanied
by nostalgia or mild regret. A pastoral minister can assist by listening
and providing security and affirmation. More significant conflict resolution may lead to guilt, depression and even despair. The appropriate pastoral response may be referral to a competent counselor
with an appreciation for the issues of the aging.

Many of the emotional responses elicited through life review or
other experiences provide opportunities to introduce the resources
of the Christian tradition. An assurance of God's unconditional love
and, if appropriate, an opportunity for the sacrament of reconciliation are obvious responses to expressions of guilt or despair. Security
needs or difficulty in making a decision may suggest a conversation or
prayer focused on the providence of God. Religious symbols can

facilitate the tasks of aging persons by providing a link with the past as well as being a concrete reminder of hope in the future. It is important to remember that the primary function of religious arti- facts in the life of the aging has little to do with theology and much to do with expressing the unique meaning they have given to their lives.

Ritual activities, familiar or new, are powerful expressions in ministry with the elderly. Even those who have a language impair- ment can frequently sing familiar hymns and become involved in a community ritual. Anointing of the sick should be ritualized and celebrated in a community setting whenever possible. Spontaneous prayer can also be a means of recognizing and affirming an individ- ual's worth in content and in the one-to-one attention it suggests.

Alongside the minister's care for the elderly, the elderly are a gift to pastoral care. Insofar as pastoral ministers strive to find their identities in accomplishments and effecting change, the elderly con- front them with the reality of the vocation to truly care. Caring for the aged is an invitation to enter the world of the weak in compan- ionship, an invitation to stay present to those who suffer when noth- ing can be done. Caring for the aged is an invitation to form a commu- nity of people facing the harsh realities of finite existence. To stand with those who suffer, be present to their pain, share their anxieties, stand in awe and silence before the mystery of death is an invitation to come in touch with their own brokenness, their own fears and doubts. The elderly demonstrate that pastoral care is not given, but is given and received in a mutuality when two are aware of their finite existence and mortality and open for the healing gifts of the other.

In the end, however, pastoral ministry with the aged is incredi- ble if the importance of understanding the psychological, sociologi- cal, and theological aspects of aging is exaggerated and the impact of cultural assumptions, symbols, and goals goes unrecognized. The aging person's interpretation of what is happening to her or him is significantly conditioned by the values and meanings inherent in his or her environment. Thus, the pastoral minister is called to both create and express a context of meaning within which the elderly can grow toward death.

Notes

1. Don S. Browning, *The Moral Context of Pastoral Care* (Philadel- phia: The Westminster Press, 1976), p. 97.
2. Rev. Charles Curran, "Aging: A Theological Perspective," in

Aging and the Human Spirit, ed. by Carol LeFevre and Perry LeFevre (Chicago: Exploration Press, 1981), pp. 68–82.

3. William M. Clements, *Care and Counseling of the Aging,* Creative Pastoral Care and Counseling Series (Philadelphia: Fortress Press, 1979), p. 30.

4. Robert N. Butler and Myrna I. Lewis, *Aging and Mental Health: Positive Psychological and Biomedical Approaches* (St. Louis: The C. V. Mosby Company, 1982), p. 58.

Cyrilla Zarek, O.P.

Parish Health Care:
Unique Needs, Special Responses

The unique needs and special responses of parish health care ministry can be approached through a basic five-step process. Although parishes differ and certain variables exist among them, any parish can apply the following five steps:

1. *Locate* the sick, the frail elderly and the homebound.

2. *Assess* their needs and those of their families.

3. *Execute* an appropriate pastoral response.

4. *Evaluate* the effectiveness of the first three steps.

5. *Revise* the process.

The effectiveness of this process is contingent upon the support and promotion of parish leadership. This leadership includes the pastor, the associates and staff working as a team. Each should be involved in the ministry to some degree. Nevertheless, more and more pastors along with their staffs realize the importance of professional competence as well as spiritual orientation and good will in sustaining a healthy Christian community. It is essential that the major responsibility for this pastoral task belongs to one member of the staff, preferably a professional health care minister serving as the coordinator of pastoral care to the sick, the elderly and the homebound.

The coordinator is expected to demonstrate the competencies stated in the NACC revised standards for advanced certification in parish health care ministry. They include the following:

1. to function as a peer with other members of the parish team;

2. to have an integrated knowledge of current church law regarding liturgy and sacraments that will enable one to function pastorally in a parish setting;

3. to have sufficient listening skills that will enhance effective parish ministry;

4. to have sufficient creative skills to establish a worshiping environment;

5. to be pastorally sensitive to the life, grief and death experience of the parish community;

6. to be aware of professional resources when referral is appropriate;

7. to demonstrate a personal emotional balance and a spiritual maturity that will be a source of nurturance to the parish community.[1]

In addition the coordinator should have some knowledge of the aging process and its implications since much of this ministry concerns working with the sick elderly. It is the coordinator who can best facilitate the five step process in collaboration with the parish staff. When this is agreed upon by the staff, the process is initiated.

Locating the Sick

As basic step one indicates, in parish health care ministry there is a need to locate the sick, the frail elderly and the homebound. Where can these people be located? Many are in hospitals, in nursing homes, in homes for the aged, and in residences for the developmentally handicapped. Most, however, are in their own homes—i.e. the chronically ill, the terminally ill, and the frail elderly confined to their homes are growing in number. These separated parishioners, institutionalized or homebound, are desperately in need of the loving, healing, saving touch of Jesus. Parish health care ministers must seek them out in the name of Jesus and in the name of the church. The term "pastoral care" comes from the image of the good shepherd. It is the good shepherd who leaves the ninety-nine in order to find the one in need (Lk 15:4). To implement locating the sick, it is important for the coordinator to know and be known by the parishioners. With them, especially the long-time parishioners, the search begins and contacts are started. Next, contacts are made with neighbors and family members. Speaking at weekly liturgies, writing bulletin articles, talking to a senior citizens club and other organizations, the coordinator is not only recognized but informed. The parish staff, especially the priests, can support and reinforce these efforts to locate those needing pastoral care. In homilies and other instructions, parishioners need to be reminded that through the sacraments of initiation—baptism, confirmation and eucharist—they are called to engage in the ministry of the church. This responsibility needs special emphasis to awaken other-centeredness in the Christian community. Although some health care facilities notify the parishes when parishioners are admitted, those confined to their own homes seldom contact the parish. Therefore, it is essential to enlist the help of the entire parish in locating the sick, the frail elderly, and the homebound. Often parishioners find much satisfaction participating in this first step.

Assessing the Needs

After learning who the sick parishioners are and where they are, the next step is to assess their needs and the needs of their families. This is most successfully done in an initial visit. This visit should be friendly, and in no way infringing upon the privacy of the person. Pertinent information should be obtained. The home and family situation should be noted. This data is later recorded on a form and filed in the coordinator's office.

Name: _____ Phone: _____

Address: _____

Place of visit: _____ Date: _____

Disablement: _____ Age: _____

Married: _____ Widowed: _____ Separated: _____ Divorced: _____

Single: _____

Living Alone: _____ With Family: _____ Who: _____

Basic needs not being met: _____

Degree of confinement:

Bed-fast ____ Some mobility ____ Crutches ____ Walker ____ Wheel Chair ____

Gets out occasionally ____ Doctor ____ Treatment Center ____

Hospital ____ Church ____

Open to pastoral visits _____ Sacraments _____

General status of care giver _____

Attached to this should be another form where dates and brief notes of subsequent visits can be recorded.

All the requested initial information may not be available at the first encounter. Whatever is made known assists in activating the needs assessment. The level of needs assessment that develops depends upon the competence of the person making the assessment. In parish health care ministry, that person's primary focus is to assess spiritual needs. Some training and experience are demanded to handle this. Three excellent resources for this second step are:

1. Leo Stanford's tape, "Pastoral Care, Preparing the Way of the Lord."[2]

2. Paul Pruyser's book, *The Minister as Diagnostician.*[3]

3. William Oglesby's article, "Referral as Pastoral Care."[4]

Seeking Appropriate Response

Assessing needs is done obviously for the purpose of responding to disabled parishioners. Hence, needs assessment requires a hard look at resources in order to execute an appropriate pastoral response. This step includes: (a) parishioners serving as pastoral ministers, (b) local hospitals and nursing homes, (c) local community services, (d) diocesan agencies and offices, (e) local seminaries. These do not exhaust possible resources. They do, however, suggest what may be available. The availability of resources will certainly vary from parish to parish and from diocese to diocese. Therefore, it is important for the coordinator to research, to know and to use when appropriate the local resources that are available.

Parishioners are the essential resources—people needing people and people responding to people. Parishioners are needed to share this ministry. Parishioners can become pastoral ministers by selection, formation, and empowerment. While selection, formation and empowerment are the work of the Spirit, they are expressed through the pastoral staff and in a special way through the coordinator. The pastoral staff should assist in the selection of parishioners. The coordinator is responsible for the formation program with the initial training and the ongoing development of parishioners serving in this ministry. *Training Pastoral Visitors*[5] by Francis Lambert and *Handbook for Ministers of Care*[6] by Marilyn Kofler, S.P. and Kevin O'Connor are especially helpful. The coordinator carefully assigns pastoral ministers to specific disabled parishioners. The coordinator and the parish staff are responsible for the empowerment, support and encouragement of these committed parishioners.

An awareness of local resources is crucial to a dynamic pastoral response. Pastoral care departments of neighboring hospitals and nursing homes not only offer direct pastoral services to parishioners who are patients, but also act as a liaison between them and the parish. Thus, continuity of pastoral care is facilitated. In addition, pastoral care personnel and other health care professionals from these facilities may conduct educational sessions for the ministry formation program. Parishioners who are nurses working in these institutions may be willing to work in programs like the parish monthly blood pressure check.

Other community services may be available through the Department of Family Services, the Department of Human Services, the American Cancer Society, A.A., food pantries and shelters, to name a few. Admittedly this moves into the area of social care. However, in parishes where no formal social care program exists, some knowledge of what these resources provide is valuable to the coordinator and to the pastoral ministers working with parishioners who are in need of these services.

Tying into diocesan resources such as Catholic Charities, the Center for Development in Ministry, the Office of Health Affairs, and others can also augment the pastoral response plan both in terms of direct service and in educational programs. In *Coordinating Parish Ministries*,[7] published by the Department of Personnel Services of the Archdiocese of Chicago, the profiles developed for professional parish ministers include that of the coordinator of the ministry of care. Those who worked on this profile saw themselves as "professionals trained in pastoral care of the sick. We assume responsibility for selection, training and development of ministers who provide a ministry of presence, prayer and sacrament. We coordinate ministry to those parishioners who are sick, elderly, homebound and bereaved and to their families. We are called and graced by God and commissioned by the faith community to share in the healing ministry of Jesus, the Good Shepherd."

Evaluation and Revision

The keys for keeping the first three steps operating effectively are evaluation at regular intervals and revision as needed. It is suggested that these two steps be taken every four months in the beginning. Then as the parish health care ministry develops and becomes well established, twice a year may be sufficient for evaluating and revising. The importance of these two steps cannot be overemphasized. To avoid evaluating and revising is wasteful of personal resources and causes decline in morale. The following forms may assist in this process, but in no way preclude other evaluative methods or tools.

I. LOCATING
A. Method Used

Approximate Number Located

Bulletin   _____

Talks at Liturgies   _____

Conversations after Liturgies   _____

Talks to organizations (List)   _____

_____   _____

_____   _____

Notified by Institutions (List)   _____

_____   _____

_____   _____

B. How many sick, frail elderly and homebound were not located as indicated by funerals of parishioners who had not received pastoral care?

_____

C. Who were they?

_____

D. Why did this happen?

_____

E. What action can be taken to avoid this happening in the future to other parishioners?

_____

II. ASSESSING NEEDS

Apparent accuracy of assessment as observed by:

1. The coordinator
2. The pastoral staff
3. The pastoral ministers
4. Those being served
5. Others

Although the above response is anecdotal it should be recorded in writing.

III. EXECUTING PASTORAL RESPONSE

A. Pastoral ministers
   1. Selection
      a. Was this done well by the coordinator and the pastoral staff?
      b. Are more ministers needed?
      c. If so, should others be included in recruiting, screening, and selecting?
      d. Who?
      e. How might this be done?
   2. Formation
      a. Was initial training adequate?
      b. What needs to be added or deleted?
      c. Does the ongoing development provide opportunities for large groups, small groups, and individual growthful experiences?
      d. Which educational resources used were most effective? Which might be dropped? Should something be added? What?
   3. Assignments
      a. Were ministers appropriately placed—hospitals, nursing homes, homebound?
      b. Were ministers assigned to disabled parishioners with whom they could relate effectively?
      c. How was this determined?
      d. If change in assignment was indicated, was this done with special regard for both the disabled parishioner and the pastoral minister?

e. How might change in assignments be accomplished in the future?

4. Empowerment
   a. How have the coordinator and the pastoral staff expressed their encouragement and support?
   b. Were the pastoral ministers recognized in the bulletin and from the pulpit?
   c. What was done by way of celebration for this ministry?
   d. What might be done in the future?

B. What was the quality of the interaction between the parish and local hospitals or nursing homes?
   Could this be improved upon? How?

C. Which community services were used?
   How were they helpful?

D. Were diocesan resources drawn upon? In what way?
   Was this beneficial?

E. Were local seminary resources available? What were they?
   How did they affect the pastoral response?

The parish offers opportunities for health care ministry at many levels.

This is evidenced in its unique needs and special responses. It is the locus for consistent, ongoing pastoral care. It is indeed a special place to engage in the service of one another. It is where "efforts to foster healing, reconciling, redeeming relationships—communion with God and with one another in his kingdom—by tangible expressions of love"[8] take place.

Notes

1. *Standards for Certification (NACC)*, Revised 1985.
2. *Pastoral Care, Preparing the Way of the Lord,* Leo Stanford, Ph.D., recorded at the NACC 20th Annual Convention, Boston, 1985, Meetings Internationale, 1200 Delor Avenue, Louisville, KY 40217, (502) 634-8229.

3. *The Minister as Diagnostician*, Paul W. Pruyser. The Westminster Press, Philadelphia, PA, 1976.

4. "Referral as Pastoral Care," William B. Oglesby, Jr., *The Journal of Pastoral Care*, June 1987. Vol. XLI, No. 2, 1549 Clairmont Rd., Suite 103, Decatur, GA 30033.

5. *Training Pastoral Visitors*, Revised, June 1985. Francis E. Lambert, Office of Health Care Ministry, Archdiocese of Baltimore, 320 Cathedral Street, Baltimore, Maryland 21201.

6. *Handbook for Ministers of Care*, Marilyn Kofler, S.P. and Kevin O'Connor. 1987, Archdiocese of Chicago. Liturgy Training Publications, 1800 North Hermitage Avenue, Chicago, IL 60622, (312) 486-7008.

7. *Coordinating Parish Ministries*, Gerard T. Broccolo, Susan C. Rosenbach, S.S.S.F., Lucien T. Roy and Lia L. Woll, S.L.W., 1987, The Chicago Catholic Publishing Co., 1144 W. Jackson Blvd., Chicago, IL 60607, (312) 243-1300.

8. *In Service of One Another*, Pastoral Letter on Ministry, Joseph Cardinal Bernardin, Archbishop of Chicago, 1985, The Chicago Catholic Publishing Co., 1144 W. Jackson Blvd., Chicago, IL 60607, (312) 243-1300.

Bibliography

Calhoun, Gerald J., S.J. *Pastoral Companionship: Ministry with Seriously-Ill Persons and Their Families*. Paulist Press, New York/Mahwah, 1986.

McGee, Nancy. *Health Care Ministers: New Parish Ministries*. Winston Press, Inc., Minneapolis, 1983.

Reimer, Lawrence D. and James, T. Wagner. *The Hospital Handbook: A Practical Guide to Hospital Visitation*. Morehouse Barlow, Wilton, 1984.

Weber, Herbert F. *The Parish Help Book: A Guide to Social Ministry in the Parish*. Ave Maria Press, Notre Dame, 1983.

Florence Flynn Smithe

General Health Care Ministry

It is Sunday night in a large midwest hospital. In the coronary care unit a ninety year old patient is dying. This heart attack is his first major illness. Surrounding him, and in the hallway outside of his room, are four generations of his family. He is deeply loved and respected for his great wisdom. They are broken-hearted; they are trying to say goodbye to him in this life and surrender him to the mysteries of eternal life. The nurse asks the operator to page the chaplain to be with the family.

On the next floor another patient is dying. This fifty year old woman is alone. She is dying of cancer. It is the final assault upon her body. For thirty years she has struggled with the disease of alcoholism. She is broken in body, mind and spirit. She is utterly alone. The chaplain is called. The patient is comforted by her ministry.

In the emergency room, a teenager is dead. Carbon monoxide; a suicide note had been found. He felt himself a failure. In a nearby waiting room his parents, family and friends are gathering. Terror, grief and guilt engulf them. The chaplain will be there soon.

In the maternity ward, a beautiful, perfectly formed baby girl comes into this world. Her birth brings little joy. The baby's father had left her mother and their five young children recently. He has been out of work and severely depressed. The doctor writes one final order on his patient's chart. "Pastoral care to see patient in the A.M."

In the newborn intensive care unit a severely deformed baby boy is fighting for life. His middle-aged parents had longed for a child for over a decade. This will be their only child. He will not live beyond this day. The chaplain will respond to the parents' request for baptism. He will listen to their cries of anguish as they search for the reasons why. What had they done wrong during the pregnancy? What is God punishing them for?

While the types of illness treated in the general hospital this night may be commonly seen, the experience of each patient and the family facing that illness is unique. They cover the full spectrum of

114

life, from birth until death. As seen in the previous examples, the chaplain must be open to the extraordinary aspects of each human struggle.

To *assume* that it may not be too difficult for a family whose ninety year old great-grandfather is dying would be to miss the opportunity to minister to a family at a crossroads in their life.

To *assume* that a fifty year old woman from the community would have family and friends at her bedside as she is dying would be to miss the opportunity to be with her in these precious moments.

To *assume* that the chaplain could do something to change how the family and friends of the dead teenager are feeling would be to "overstand" (to look down upon) rather than to seek to *understand* them.

If we *assume* that the mother with a healthy new baby is happy, we may lose the opportunity *to be* with her in her anguish, to hear the secrets of her heart.

If the chaplain *assumed* that the parents of the baby in NICU were needing his absolution in order to be convinced that they were not responsible for their child's problems, he might be enabling them to avoid confronting their necessary guilt before they can let it go.

The chaplain in general hospital ministry approaches each new encounter, not as one sent to find solutions to their problems but rather as a vessel, open to receive, to listen and to share in the pain. They are open to *be with* others in their sacred space. The vessel has windows as well, to allow the reflection of God's love and grace to emerge from within toward those to whom we minister.

Although the title of this chapter might imply a vast text, we will highlight just a few areas of ministry for chaplains. The books referenced will serve as additional resources.[1]

Newborn Death

Historically

Until five or six decades ago, and from the beginning of time, the process of birthing took place in the privacy of one's home. Since maternity care has moved into the hospital, the health of mother and child has been greatly enhanced. However, the issue of emotional and spiritual support of the parents when an infant died became somewhat distorted. Hospital medical and pastoral staff, responding to the enormous pain of parents and to their own shared anguish, tried to diminish the parents' suffering. Consequently it became common practice for the nursing staff to "spirit" away the body of a child lost in miscarriage, stillbirth or infant death before the parents could even see it. If the parents would ask, they might be reassured by the physician: "If it was my wife I would not allow her to see *it!*"

Chaplains strive to diminish that kind of fear sometimes associated with the physical remains of a dead infant or fetus. The body is not a dangerous object! We know that in the course of nature not all life conceived will survive. Some would refer to miscarriage as life's way of correcting an accident of nature. And yet the use of the word "natural" in relationship to miscarriage is awkward. Clearly, the death of an infant is not perceived as natural by family and staff who witness the tragedy. This new life should be lived!

We are moving away from those "unnatural" procedures of denial that separated parents from the necessary involvement in activities related to their newborn's death and burial, and are striving to enable them to participate more naturally. Parents of infants who have died have reflected on their experiences and taught us to return to more natural ways of "being" for them at the time of their infant's death and in those precious moments that follow.

Beginning in the early 1970s, some of these parents began to meet together and form mutual support groups. In this "safe" place they felt free to share the emotional and spiritual feelings of devastation that they had known since the death of their child. Some had been unable to resolve their grief, feeling unfinished months and even years beyond their child's death. In relation to this issue a common cry was heard: "How could I have said good-bye to my baby when I had never been allowed to say hello to her?" These feelings of unresolved conflict within sometimes became the breeding ground for distress and dis/ease, escalating marital discord (a significant increase in the divorce rate is associated with infant death) and relationship problems with family and friends who couldn't understand. Many of these bereaved parents were unhappy, uneasy and unhealthy.

Not only did they feel resistance to their efforts to grieve from hospital staff, but reactions from society and even their parish church may have added to their confusion. For instance, family and friends may not have anticipated the depth of their grief. They presumed that since the one who died was "only a baby," the parents didn't really know the child and consequently their grieving would be minimized. Their parish priest may have told them that they didn't "need" to have a mass for their dead baby's funeral, and in fact may have suggested that the funeral director and the baby's father could take care of everything at the cemetery. The pain of these parents was compounded. Their church was not present to their anguish in a pastoral or liturgical sense.

The theological questions abound when an infant dies. Never is the wonder and majesty of God's love more evident than when loving parents behold their newborn child. Conversely never is a sense of God's absence more profound than at the birth of a stillborn infant or an infant afflicted with severe abnormalities. In these awesome experiences of life we are often plunged to the depths of our beings, where we encounter the ultimate mysteries of life. Our spirits demand answers. Is this child's death God's will? Who is being punished? For what? Why these parents? Why now?

The chaplain and medical staff share in the anguish of these unanswered questions. No doubt this inevitable emotional and spiritual pain is a part of the reason that C.P.E. student chaplains, and staff chaplains as well, will sometimes recognize their personal resistance and anxiety regarding ministry in obstetrics and newborn intensive care.

Current teaching acknowledges that the chaplain and medical staff need to be aware of their own feelings regarding death. However, intense personal pain, frustration, and anger are still often suppressed. We want to be available to support one another in our own humanness, and yet personal resistance and/or time constraints can divert our good intentions. If we are out of touch with our own feelings, it is then difficult to be authentically present to the feelings of the parents.

Perhaps it is a question of professionalism that keeps us from mutual support. We may feel alone and vulnerable with the powerful personal feelings that struggle to emerge. Somehow it seems too threatening for medical staff and chaplains to acknowledge their own feelings, let alone to share them with others. It may be that our own personal unresolved grief and loss are the source of the profound pain and dis/ease felt alongside the pain of those we minister to. Ideally, staff should also have a support group, the same kind of "safe place" that is so useful to bereaved parents.

Clearly there are other sides to this story. There have always been those who know quite "naturally" how to minister sensitively to the unique concerns of parents whose children had died. We continue to grow from their wisdom and understanding of this process.

However we might expand our thinking even further if we would consider an important analogy.

The sacredness of life, from the moment of conception, is central to the essence of our faith. Protecting the right to life of the fetus, living within its mother's womb is the impassioned and public plea of our church leaders. And yet, parents who have lost a child in miscarriage, stillbirth or infant death may experience an attitude from clergy, medical staff, family and friends that their loss was really "no big deal," or that it was "only a fetus." It was as though "nobody" was really there. The reality that "somebody" was indeed there is fundamental and needs to be reflected in our ministry to parents who have lost their infant to an accident of nature, as well as to those who grieve after they have chosen abortion. Consequently, chaplains may find themselves involved in ministry that revolves around issues of abortion or infant death even decades following the event. Patients telling their life stories may reveal a profound woundedness regarding their unresolved grief. Chaplains may be an important instrument of healing as they enable the patient to go back and release deeply painful memories. In some cases a ceremony of naming, letting go or forgiveness may be useful tools toward resolution. If we are to be consistent in our beliefs, then we must be more intentional about supporting all parents who grieve infant loss.

This ministry provides another powerful affirmation of the pro-life issue. The more we ritualize and personalize the grieving process for a dead fetus/infant, the more viable is our statement regarding the sacred nature of all life within the womb.

Procedures. In most areas of the hospital the chaplain focuses on *being* with the bereaved and not on *doing* for them. However, it can be helpful if the following details are attended to when an infant dies. (See Addendum #1.) Of primary importance is for the chaplain to learn from the medical staff whether the death is of a liveborn or stillborn infant or the miscarriage of a fetus. Appropriate hospital and religious policies can then be explained to the parents.

1. *Privacy.* Endeavor to create a safe and private environment (see Addendum #3) where the parents will be free to begin to express their feelings and emotions. Whenever possible they should be encouraged to see and hold their baby's body. If the mother's physical condition prohibits this, she should be given the opportunity again when she is more stable. To reassure the parents the chaplain may see the baby first, perhaps preparing them for the experience by describing the appearance of the body.

2. *Baptism.* The issue of a dead fetus/infant is a delicate one. It is important to grasp the deeper meaning of the traditional theological approach and of pastoral sensitivity.

Many parents ask that their child be baptized even though it was stillborn. The traditional theological approach does not allow this since baptism was traditionally seen as the cleansing from original sin. That baptism also incorporates the child into the community of believers, the mystical body of Christ, was always accepted but often not emphasized. Contemporary theology focuses more explicitly on this incorporation into the community of faith. Although this aspect alone does not warrant the sacramental baptism of a stillborn, pastoral sensitivity offers many openings for appropriate prayers or paraliturgical expressions which deepen the bond between the child and the grieving family.

Meaningful ceremonies provide ways to utilize symbols of our faith tradition which give a special dignity to the child who is already totally united with God in his eternal joy. Parents and/or godparents may want to participate in choosing readings or prayers for this ceremony. Flowers or candles which might be used can become for the parents priceless keepsakes.

3. *Photographs.* Pictures taken of a dead infant may at first sound morbid or distasteful. However, as emotional healing takes place they may become a precious possession. If the body is badly deformed the parents may at first refuse them but later request them to establish the truth. Their thoughts and dreams may be creating images far worse than the reality.

4. *Extended Family.* Whenever possible, with the parents' approval, siblings and grandparents of the dead newborn should also be given an opportunity to see the body of the baby. They too were preparing for this new life to come into the family and may benefit by being allowed to enter into the grieving process at this point.

5. *Reverse Transport.* When a newborn dies in a hospital away from the hospital where their mother remains a patient, the parents should still be given the option to view their baby's body. This unusual and rather complicated process can be accomplished with the assistance of the funeral director. They might stop at the hospital where the mother is a patient, after picking up the infant's remains and before proceeding to the funeral home. This activity can be an important step toward helping the mother to accept the reality of her child's death. If possible, this chaplain can facilitate the availability of the family's clergyman or other chaplain to be with them at that time.

6. *Disposition of Remains.* This question must be addressed within the guidelines of each family's beliefs and each hospital's policies.

(a) *Hospital Disposition.* Some institutions still believe that the "humane" solution is for the hospital to arrange for the disposition. This practice is generally discouraged for a newborn death or still-birth. It takes away the responsibility and opportunity for the family to enter into the necessary funeral rites.

However, the body of a fetus, under twenty weeks' gestation, is usually disposed of through cremation or burial with other fetal remains by the hospital. Occasionally one of these families will choose to make private funeral arrangements, but it is uncommon. One problem is that no birth certificate is issued for one born dead weighing under one pound one ounce. Therefore it is not possible to obtain a death certificate, necessary for a burial permit. This fact, coupled with the attitude that "nobody" is there, may point toward the more convenient option of hospital disposition.

(b) *Private Burial/Cremation.* Some parents realize that they could not allow the hospital to dispose of the body of their baby, and yet they do not feel it would be appropriate to have a funeral. Consequently the father may accompany the funeral director to the cemetery alone, perhaps feeling that he is sparing his wife additional pain. Mothers tend to resent being excluded and find their sense of being cheated intensified.

(c) *Funeral or Memorial Service.* Simple arrangements can be made with dignity and warmth. Clergy, family and friends can be there not only to support the parents but also to deal with their own grief. Having participated in this ritual, family and friends are more inclined to be able to continue to share in the parents' anguish in the difficult months ahead. The funeral brings the life and death of the person who has died into focus.

7. *Support Follow-Up.* In ideal situations the chaplain, with other medical team members, might offer follow-up ministry to bereaved parents. Occasional phone calls or notes can help to reassure them that their baby is remembered. Regularly scheduled meetings with other bereaved parents can provide that safe place where parents feel free to share not only their anguish but also their healing.

8. *Booklet.* It is helpful if the chaplain can give the parents some written material that will restate these suggestions.[2] Initially they may be in shock and unable to comprehend what is being said. The mother may pick up a booklet left at her bedside when she is ready to address the questions.

Being able to stay with these painful situations is often very difficult for the chaplain, who may encounter several such crises in a brief period of time. The task is to be gentle and caring, not to rush the parents to make decisions but simply to be with them, guiding them toward their inner strengths, the resources of their faith and the options set before them.

Obviously, it is important that the area clergy, lay ministers and funeral directors be aware that chaplains are making these suggestions to bereaved parents. Their collective sensitivity to these concerns can be enhanced through collaborative community education outreach programs.

It is important to acknowledge another paradox here. Clearly we are suggesting more fully developing the role of the chaplain in obstetrics and newborn intensive care. And yet at the same time we are confronted with the sharp decline in the numbers of Catholic priests. Consequently it is unrealistic to presume that Catholic patients will be ministered to by Catholic priest chaplains and their own parish priest.

As we expand our knowledge and competence regarding this ministry we must also expand our understanding of who the proper ministers might be.

First of all it would seem unlikely and even inappropriate to expect parish priests to come into the hospital for these obstetric emergencies. We can look to hospital chaplains and medical staff to respond in a pastoral and caring manner.

It is our expectation that the hospital chaplain is a person trained and certified in the process of clinical pastoral education. These chaplains may be of the Protestant or Jewish faith traditions as well, since their preparation for chaplaincy includes a sensitivity to particular denominational concerns.

These chaplains may be ordained priests, pastors, deacons, religious, or lay persons. They may be male or female. It is obvious that blending the particular sensitivity of women ministers into the area of obstetrics can provide an added resource.

The possibilities of shared ministries might extend to the parish as well. Perhaps each parish could have a particular staff person or a married couple who would have training and experience to prepare them for this ministry. They might be available to parents who are experiencing a problem pregnancy and visit with them soon after delivery. They could assist the bereaved parents with funeral arrangements and liturgy and be there for them to offer ongoing support.

The important fact here is that "someone" be there for parents who have experienced miscarriage or infant death.

This is our call. Bereaved parents are teaching us to respond to it more clearly with competence and compassion, as a sign of God's own presence to his children in their suffering.

Cancer and Heart Disease

Other areas of frequent concern for hospital chaplains are ministry to patients dealing with cancer[3] and heart disease.[4]

For many, these words "cancer" and "heart disease" are *synonymous with death.* They strike terror in our hearts. Who among us does not dread these diseases? To say "I have cancer" or "I have heart disease" can surface the profound question, "Am I dying?"

Ministry in a general hospital brings us into relationship with individuals struggling with these questions on a daily basis. It is essential that chaplains be in touch with the highly charged nature of the words "cancer" and "heart disease," so that they can be alert to this issue for patients and for themselves.

In reality both words are umbrella words covering a broad spectrum of diseases with many variations and degrees of severity. For example, some forms of skin cancer may be curable and rather simple to treat, while certain forms of leukemia are extremely painful to treat and often fatal. Likewise many forms of heart disease, i.e. mitral value prolapse, are usually treated successfully, while the patient in need of a heart transplant is certainly in a life threatening situation.

As tests and procedures are completed, patients are often overwhelmed by the foreign language of the medical world. A major function of the chaplain's ministry can be to help patients and medical staff hear one another and to *clarify the language* and the confusion felt by the patient. Countless, needless hours of anguish are experienced by patients and families who hear the words "cancer/ heart disease" and then never really hear anything else that is said. The chaplain who enters into the suffering of his patients can help them to know if their fears are based on facts or upon the terror unleashed by the language of the diagnosis. In some hospitals a meeting can be convened with patient, family, physicians, nurses, and chaplains present together to establish better communications. In hospitals where this type of conference is not possible the chaplain may seek the assistance of one of these professional medical staff persons to meet at length with the patient/family. In either type of meeting the chaplain can enable all to truly *hear* one another. It is equally important for the medical staff to hear the patient's feelings as well.

While those moments of uncertainty unfold, there is an important dynamic occurring. The relationship between chaplain and patient is developing and the role of the chaplain is being established. The patient begins to recognize that he or she can share doubts and fears, hopes and dreams, without being judged. The crisis of hospitalization often brings these feelings to the surface. It can be very good to have someone with whom we can share these depths of emotion and feeling. The chaplain communicates faithfulness. "I'll be here for you." This commitment can establish trust, which is often an important concern of the patient. "Who is going to stick by me if the going gets rough?" "Can I be a person of value if I can not be useful and productive?" "Will I have to go through it alone?"

For others, this crisis is the beginning of a long process of treatment, healing, and learning to live with the limitations which may be imposed by the disease. This can be a very frustrating period, experienced like a roller coaster ride: feeling stronger and full of hope, and in the same day feeling empty and hopeless. The coronary patient may look healthy and rested and yet be quite disabled. The cancer patient may look very bad while being cured with chemotherapy and radiation. Simultaneously they may experience temporary regression due to the side-effects of the treatment. Anxiety is often very evident in the patient during this period. The unknown future fosters intense fear. "What next?" This uneasiness is often demonstrated in hostile behavior toward staff and family. The patient doesn't seem to trust anyone, not even the chaplain. Such patients are very difficult to be with, and staff tend to avoid non-essential contact with them. Just as the patient anticipated, support may decrease when the going gets rough. This is a particularly important and difficult time for the chaplain. It is hard to be faithful over the long haul!

Patients dealing with these life-threatening illnesses do a lot of soul-searching. This process frequently leads them to speak about significant experiences and people in their lives. Remembering and telling one's own story can be very healing. It is often the privilege of the hospital chaplain to be the listener, as a patient searches for and proclaims the meaning and value of their life. In the reflective process that may follow, themes and similar threads begin to appear. The patient needs to make decisions. In facing the reality of his or her dis/ease and new limitations, a new lifestyle must emerge. This requires letting go of old behaviors. Change is indeed very hard work.

This is an important time to offer a ministry of compassion.[5] At this point, everyone is telling the patient what *to do* and how to feel. Patients may appreciate someone who will feel their emotional and spiritual struggle. They may be trying to let go of what was unhealthy and then to respect what is (to let it be). They may recognize a need to further develop their understanding of their relationship to God in light of their present situation.

The chaplain, ministering to patients with such life-threatening diseases, will surely come into a relationship with the patients' families. This is a very important part of our ministry. When a member of the family is seriously ill, the family circle is experiencing brokenness, with all members feeling the impact of the news. They are concerned, not only for their loved one and other family members, but for themselves.

"Will my husband survive?" "Will I be able to provide the long term care he will require?" "How will I manage all the bills?" "Why is God doing this to us?"

The hospital chaplain may be a somewhat "anonymous" caring person. Consequently, the patient's wife may feel "safe" to express her own concerns and needs. Loved ones often stifle their own cries of pain, feeling guilty about thinking of themselves when their family member is suffering. The chaplain can validate the importance of the family expressing their needs, and help them to explore ways to try to respond to those needs.

Looking back over our lives many of us can identify times when as children we were shut out of the truth regarding the illness and or death of a family member. Adults chose to shield us from the harsh realities of life. "Let them enjoy being children; they'll grow up soon enough." However, the children know that something is wrong. Family life is disrupted; they feel an unspoken sense of danger. There are no boundaries for this fear because the children do not have access to the facts. Their imagination becomes the tool with which they attempt to construct reality. Nightmares, withdrawal, or behavior disorders may develop. Alert to the needs of children, the chaplain seeks to involve them and to enable the family to share the truth with them. Children should be given *choices* regarding visits to a sick or dying relative, as well as participation in the wake and funeral. In this process children are given the opportunity to give and receive support within the family. They may experience emotional and spiritual growth. They can then feel themselves to be persons capable of coping with the realities of life.

In these situations, the ministry of the patient's home parish/

congregation can also be a valuable resource. When a hospitalized patient and his or her family are linked back to the parish family, we have completed an important circle.

The Dying Patient—Long Term vs. Sudden

The cancer patient may be dying slowly over a period of many weeks or months. In contrast, the cardiac patient's death often occurs suddenly in the crisis of cardiac arrest. The cancer patient may be in a hospice-like setting surrounded by family, friends and familiar possessions. The coronary patient often dies in an emergency room or coronary care unit. There he or she will be separated from family and surrounded by the high technology of intensive care. It is obvious that it is possible for the cancer patient to die in a more "natural" environment. For the cancer patient there is more control and time in which decisions can be carefully considered. Questions can be pondered: "Will I continue to accept chemotherapy and other treatments?" "Will I remain in the hospital, in a hospice center or at home?" "If I do go home will I be brought to the hospital when death is imminent?" It can be helpful to the patient/family if the chaplain would suggest that they look specifically at that option. In some cases a family will call for their community paramedics as their loved one is dying and then be shocked that the patient has been placed on life support in the ambulance or in the hospital emergency room. This may actually be contrary to the intentions of the patient/family but is the automatic response of emergency medical teams. The process of dying with dignity can be greatly assisted if patients/families are encouraged to clearly communicate their wishes to the necessary people.

Obviously these issues can be more difficult for the cardiac patient to deal with. Often they are unprepared and unable to speak for themselves. The more complex ethical questions of their life and death fall into the hands of the family and medical team. The value of each one of us preparing a living will (see Addendum #3) becomes clearer with the continued advancement of medical technology.

To die suddenly is the prayer of many—"Lord, when it's my turn, make it fast." However, the chaplain working with cancer patients who are dying learns that the long process of dying can bring a rich peace and joy to patients, families, and staff. As the journey unfolds a very significant dynamic may emerge. Patients find themselves with increasingly large segments of quiet time alone. At first their reaction to this may be to feel useless. "What good am I? I cannot *do* anything." This may be another important moment of ministry. The chaplain may guide patients to recognize that as they let go of their need to *do* they can find the freedom to simply *be*, to discover inner solitude. As their needs to attend to the external world diminish, they may have new psychic space and energy which can now be used for the journey within. This is, of course, the most important movement of our lives!

The chaplain may be the "one" chosen by the patient to share this process with. It is indeed a sacred trust given and received. The space is now open to be filled with God's love.

The patient's dreams[6] may offer important insights for this inward journey. This valuable gift of the Spirit is often carelessly disregarded. The chaplain may open the possibility of valuing the dreams by inquiring if patients ever remember their dreams. Patients are often very grateful for this permission to share and explore their dreams. They may discover in them additional guidances for the process of their inner healing and for the journey to eternal life.

Even as the body is dying much new life can be experienced. As patients move inward they may discover the Spirit of God there in a profound way, not known to them when they were physically well and too busy to find their way in. It is possible then to feel and experience God's love, to feel his forgiveness and to forgive him for the things we don't understand. An important outgrowth of these things can be additional healing of broken or damaged relationships with family and friends.

The work of dying can be accomplished in this way—Saying goodbye, letting go of this life and moving toward God, our creator and redeemer. Truly it is out of the suffering of patient, family and staff that this new life is experienced. It can be an incarnational experience.

Patients who feel God is absent in their dying may discover him in the compassionate presence of the hospital chaplain, the caring medical team, and their family and friends.

Notes

1. Howard Clinebell, *Pastoral Care and Counseling*, Abingdon Press, 1984; Lawrence Holst, ed., *The Role of the Chaplain Today*, Crossroad, 1985; Morton Kelsey, *Caring*, Paulist Press, 1984; Henri Nouwen, *Creative Ministry*, Doubleday, 1971; Regis Duffy, O.F.M., *A Roman Catholic Theology of Pastoral Care*, Fortress Press, 1983;

Reimer & Wagner, *The Hospital Handbook*, Morehouse Barlow Company, 1984; Ernest Bruder, *Ministering to Deeply Troubled People*, Fortress Press, 1964.

2. *Newborn Death*, Centering Corporation, Box 3367, Omaha, Neb. 68103-0367.

3. O. Carl Simonton, *Getting Well Again*, St. Martin's Press, 1980.

4. George Patterson, *The Cardiac Patient*, Augsburg, 1978.

5. Matthew Fox, *A Spirituality Named Compassion*, Winston Press, 1979.

6. C.G. Jung, *Dreams*, Princeton, 1974.

Addendum #1

Lutheran General Hospital
NICU
Checklist for Parents Experiencing Neonatal Death

Mother's Name _____ Father's Name _____

Date	Check ☐ To Indicate Completion (when appropriate)	Signature
	☐ Date & Time of Expiration Documented	
	☐ Saw baby when born and/or after delivery ___ Mother ___ Father	
	☐ Touched and/or held baby ___ Mother ___ Father ___ Grandparents ___ Siblings	
	☐ Was Privacy provided? ___ Yes ___ No	
	☐ Photo Taken	
	☐ Butterfly to Mother's room door (if LGH Baby)	
	☐ Previous loss ___ Miscarriage ___ Stillbirth ___ Newborn _____ Weeks gestation	
	☐ Have parents named this baby? ___ Yes ___ No	
	☐ Patient Affairs notified of baby's first name	
	☐ Pastoral Care notified	
	☐ Autopsy Consent ___ Yes ___ No	
	☐ Baptism ___ Yes ___ No	
	☐ Naming Certificate ___ Yes ___ No	
	☐ Ethnic or Denominational Needs ___ Yes ___ No	
	☐ Release of Remains signed by ___ Mother ___ Father	
	☐ Value of Funeral Service discussed	
	☐ Informed about postponing funeral until Mother can attend	
	☐ Option of reverse transport of infant's body if mother still at referring hospital; explained to parents	

Addendum #2

Date: November 14, 1986

To: Pastoral Care Staff/Ministers of Communion
Visiting Clergy/Musicare Volunteers

From: Flo Smithe, Chaplain, Ob-Peds

Subject: Identification of Maternity patients experiencing infant death

The Mother-Baby Unit is instituting a protocol for assisting families who experience the loss of a baby, to work through their grief.

In addition to a check-list to be used jointly by nursing and Pastoral Care, there will be a means of identifying those mothers who have experienced a loss.

Many times hospital staff other than those who work on the unit are not aware of the family's grief. In order to communicate this information to all who enter the mother's room, whether on the maternity or another unit, we will be placing a special card with the mother's name on the door.

The card will have the usual information, but will be colored paper and have butterflies as an identifying symbol for a miscarriage, a stillborn or a neonatal death.

Please share this information at your next division or staff meeting. A copy of the butterfly identification card is displayed on the Community Clergy Board.

Addendum #3

Questions and Answers About A Living Will

Q. **What is a Living Will?**

A. A Living Will is a written statement instructing your doctor that if you ever are suffering from an incurable/terminal medical condition, that you do not want him/her to start or continue any procedures that only will serve to postpone (put off) the moment of death.

Q. **Who may write a Living Will?**

A. Any person of sound mind who is married or is 18 years of age or older, as well as any emancipated minor (person under 18 who **legally** is free to make his/her own decisions).

Q. **If I have a Living Will, can I still receive medication for pain?**

A. A Living Will does not keep your doctor from giving you medication or doing procedures to take away your pain.

Q. **What happens if I have a Living Will and I am pregnant and have an incurable condition?**

A. A Living Will has no effect during a pregnancy.

Q. **If I have a Living Will, must my doctor follow my instructions?**

A. If you have a valid Living Will, your doctor must follow your instructions. If your doctor is unable to do so because of his/her ethical or moral principles or because doing so would not be in keeping with his/her professional standards, he/she is required to refer your case to another doctor.

Q. **Are there any rules I must follow when writing a Living Will?**

A. Illinois law requires that a Living Will be entirely typed or entirely hand written and that it be written in a specific way to include certain points. We suggest you follow a sample Living Will form for Illinois which your doctor may have available or which may be obtained from the Lutheran General Hospital, Division of Pastoral Care. Call 696-6395.

Q. **Who should have a copy of my Living Will?**

A. You should give the following people a copy of your Living Will:

• Your doctor(s)
• Your next-of-kin or closest friend
• Your lawyer

Q. **Once I write my Living Will, can it be changed?**

A. You may change your Living Will at any time; however, changes to a Living Will cannot simply be written in or crossed out. Changes to your Living Will must be in the same form as the original, either typed or hand written, and attached to the original.

Q. **Can a Living Will be cancelled?**

A. A Living Will can be cancelled at any time. There are three ways to cancel a Living Will:

• By destroying or marking up the Living Will in such a way that your wish to cancel it would be clearly known.

• By writing down your wish to cancel the will, including your signature and the date. This can be done by someone else acting at your direction.

• By telling someone 18 years old or older your wish to cancel your Living Will. This person must then write down your wish to cancel the will and include his/her signature and the date.

If you decide to cancel your Living Will, you must tell your doctor and all other persons having a copy of your Living Will. This may be done in writing or by talking to each person. If you tell someone 18 years old or older that you would like to cancel your Living Will, this person must inform each person having a copy of your Living Will.

III. Pastoral Education

Dorothy Cotterell, S.U.S.C.
and William F. Nisi

Clinical Pastoral Education

The phrase "clinical pastoral education," commonly known as CPE, has come into increasing prominence during recent years. Overheard frequently on seminary campuses are: "I have my CPE this summer"; in newspaper ads for chaplains, "CPE preferred"; in a hospital dining room, "The new CPE students are here."

Clinical pastoral education, which is a unique process of theological education, can best be understood from an historical perspective.

This brief summary of the sixty year history of the Association for Clinical Pastoral Education (ACPE) highlights but does not begin to capture the rich and creative spirit or the intense and human struggle that is this movement. For those who want to delve more thoroughly into the history of the association, they are encouraged to read Robert C. Powell's *Fifty Years of Learning* and to view the video-cassette, "Sixty Years of CPE"; both can be obtained from the national office of ACPE.

If anything is clear throughout the history of ACPE, it is the belief that the art of pastoral care cannot be taught in a classroom, that persons in crisis, "living human documents," need to be experienced and studied, and that the scientific knowledge of the meaning and dynamics of human growth and development must be studied with historic and contemporary theologies. Underlying this belief is the purpose of equipping persons for ministry to a world often filled with persons who are broken in body, mind and spirit. While the belief and purpose are in retrospect a pushing and pulling unifying force, how they were to be translated into a program of theological education became, like human growth, itself a process filled with struggle and change.

The historical records indicate that around the turn of the century some efforts were made to bring theological students and clergy into supervised relationships with sick and troubled persons. While

133

these seeds were sown in the Boston area they remained dormant until the early 1920s. The "seedbed" which eventually nourished the roots of CPE was a significant period in the history of the world. The first great war had ended. The innocent idealism of the western world was crumbling and in ferment. New ideas in economics, social change, medicine, and depth psychology were challenging to the old order. Religious communities felt the assault as informed inquiry beckoned the established faith groups to take seriously the emerging human sciences.

It was in this fertile milieu that two physicians, one in Boston and one in Cincinnati, set in motion the early experiments at education outside the seminary classroom. Dr. William S. Keller, an active layman in the Episcopal Church, joined the Department of Social Service of the Diocese of Southern Ohio in 1923. He established contact with the diocesan seminary and set in motion a program where seminary students were exposed to social service activities in institutions and in the community. Keller's method was to give the students the experience of working in social agencies and then provide weekly seminars to emphasize the human predicament with the hope that religion might be more relevant to the lives of persons in crisis. While students were required to do case studies to aid the learning process, the case work was seen as a vehicle to enhance the interaction between the students and the persons in trouble. Getting out of the sheltered setting of the theological seminary and into the real world was the major thrust of the program. By 1927 what was mainly experiential learning was becoming more intentional and a curriculum was developed. The Summer School of Social Work was of nine weeks' duration and included lectures and case seminars. In 1936, Keller, with the assistance of the Rev. Joseph Fletcher, began the Graduate School of Applied Religion. The new school was a year-long program and sought to correlate the social with the theological. One of the main objectives of the school was equipping persons for more effective ministry.

If one were to write a history of medical social work, the first name that would be mentioned would be that of Dr. Richard Clarke Cabot. In the history of CPE which evolves from the Boston area, the same name occurs. Dr. Cabot gave impetus to both movements because of his interest in teaching and in using the case study as a vehicle for enhancing the educational process. Students were asked to analyze patient records and to meet with peers and instructors to discuss and to come to a better understanding of what was occurring in the lives of patients. Cabot took his educational method first to medical students, then to social work students, and finally to theological students. For him, discovering the underlying causes of patients' problems was a key which pulled the various disciplines together. Thus Cabot stressed a special diagnostic function utilizing the case method and the peer group.

One of Cabot's students was the Rev. Anton Boisen. Boisen during an acute psychotic illness had an experience which he felt was an opening in the wall that separated medicine and religion. From this powerful event, Boisen studied and prepared himself to explore the religious significance in illness. Utilizing the case method of Cabot, Boisen refined it and added to it. In 1924 Boisen became the chaplain at the Worcester State Hospital and within the year some theological students came to the hospital to learn first-hand about mental illness. The early students were given the experience of working and interviewing patients with time spent reading and in discussion groups. Boisen stressed the importance of insight and understanding of persons in trouble in contrast to Cabot, who underscored the need to teach skills and techniques.

These early educational experiments were well received and the need for an organization to guide the growth of the movement and to set standards for centers and supervisors became apparent. Thus in 1930 the Council for the Clinical Training of Theological Students was incorporated. Now there were two traditions within clinical pastoral education.

The third tradition in CPE began in the 1930s also in the Boston area. Initially it was called the New England Group and later the Institute of Pastoral Care. Austin Philip Guiles worked with Boisen and the Council and eventually became the chaplain at Massachusetts General Hospital. Later he joined the faculty at Andover-Newton Theological School as the director of clinical training. Obviously, this new venture was closely aligned with theological education and was characterized by taking CPE into the general hospital. Russell Dicks, who assumed the chaplain's position at Massachusetts General after Guiles, began to raise some new and pragmatic questions, mainly, how does one minister to persons who are sick? With this focus Dicks began to record his pastoral visits and prayers, and the "Verbatim" became a valuable tool for CPE.

Now there were three organizations for CPE. The years between the 1930s and 1967, when the three groups merged to form the Association for Clinical Pastoral Education, were years of growth toward professionalism in providing education for ministry. A key development in those years was gaining acceptance by theological schools and in turn by the various faith groups. Gaining this recognition caused the three traditions to dialogue with each other, with theological schools, and with the various faith groups. This process provided the means for the eventual merger of the groups but also caused them to take with more seriousness the theological and pastoral dimensions of CPE and to consider with more intentionality that CPE is a vital process in training persons for ministry.

As the movement has grown, what has happened to the questions that were so vital to its development? Should CPE teach skills and techniques or insights and understandings? Should the context of CPE be the psychiatric hospital, the general hospital, or the social setting where persons are in crisis? Is CPE primarily education in learning how to provide ministry to persons or is it growth for the student? Should CPE focus primarily on the dynamics in the patient or should the dynamics of the relationship including student also be examined? These questions and more are still there, but as the movement matured and became integrated, the questions became important only to clarify that CPE should provide both, and should not answer any of the questions by taking a firm position on either side. Thus CPE does teach the skills of ministering to persons in crisis and at the same time teaches insights and understanding into the person and into the student. CPE can be provided in a variety of contexts, each having a richness and a uniqueness for ministry. CPE is primarily education for ministry, but it may offer at the same time the possibility for personal growth and integration for the student.

Methods

As the history of CPE unfolded, a way of doing CPE developed. While each center and every supervisor will have unique qualities to bring to the educational process, there seems to be a common methodology to which all centers and all supervisors adhere. First there is the experiential, the setting for ministry. CPE students are very quickly assigned to function as providers of pastoral care and are expected to offer chaplaincy services to patients, families, and staff. Part of the experience for the student, the learning by doing, is the educational setting of CPE, namely the relationships that form between peers and with the supervisors. The relationships in both the experiential settings and the feelings from both contexts are the central learning ingredients for CPE.

Experience by itself is only experience. It needs to be focused by learning goals and objectives, and by *reflection*. Reflection on experience is accomplished in the clinical setting by the use of process recordings, the verbatims, and by visits to patients with the supervisor and follow-up discussion. The verbatim becomes a way of teaching the student to ponder experience and to examine it from various perspectives. In the educational setting reflection occurs with peers and the supervisors through case conferences, seminars on verbatims, and supervisory sessions. From reflection students begin to become sensitive to the experiences of patients, to the student's own feelings, and to the nature of the relationship. Questions are raised from experience and answers are sought from experience and from other sources, both clinical and theological.

Insight is a process of connecting experience to newly discovered truths about oneself or another. In the clinical setting students are exposed to new concepts about patients, their illnesses and the ways patients respond to their crises. Similarly, students are being exposed to an awareness of the importance of a person's history and the personality dynamics that stem from that history. Thus as students provide pastoral care, significant connections are made for patients to their experiences and new connections may be made to issues of faith. In the educational setting didactic learnings are provided which are being used in the clinical area. These didactic learnings are also utilized to help the students look at their own histories, personality dynamics, and faith development so that through group sharing, which includes the reflective process, the students begin to make new discoveries about themselves as persons and as pastors. Someone has said, "You see what you know." The increase of knowledge is to help students discover a framework in which to view others and themselves. Insight comes when this knowledge makes new sense in a dynamic and connective way.

Experience, reflection, insight, will hopefully lead to *action and integration*. Taking insight and using it in new ways confirms that it is indeed insight. In the clinical setting, action and integration might come through being an active professional chaplain on a healing team using oneself more fully as a person and a pastor. In the educational setting, action and integration might come through learning to supervise oneself and others with a new awareness of oneself as a person and pastor.

The following is an attempt to show the CPE process in the form of a diagram. Obviously it is a dynamic moving experience that is multidimensional.

Learning Through Clinical Pastoral Education

Clinical Setting (goals & objectives)

Educational Setting (goals & objectives)

Experience

Relationships to families, patients and staff

Relationships to peers and supervisors

Reflection

Verbatims—Process Recordings
Visits & Discussion

Case Conferences
Verbatim Seminars
Supervision Session
Theological Reflection

Insight

Discovering about illness—Crisis—effects on patients
Seeing, learning in helping patients—with dynamic issues—life histories—faith dilemmas

Didactics—lectures—Readings—Discoveries about self
—Own dynamics and history

Action/Integration

Becoming part of a healing team; using oneself as a pastor

Learning to supervise self and others; new awareness of oneself as person and pastor

---

The diagram should be read as one with dynamic ups and downs, and not as a steady growth to integration. The new experiences of doing ministry and meeting with peers and supervisors provide the constant thrust of CPE. Experience and reflection are the warp and woof of CPE with insight and integration being the occasional but life-giving precious moments. Similarly this diagram can be viewed as the same process that occurs between the chaplain and the patient, moving from experience of illness and the pastoral relationship to reflection on one's predicament and occasionally to insight and to the healing that one can discover even in the midst of illness.

Until the late 1960s, when the National Association of Catholic Chaplains (NACC) began its own training process, ACPE was the only organization that provided clinical training for clergy. Presently the National Association of Catholic Chaplains is a 3,500-member association, which was formerly an arm of the USCC but became autonomous in 1980. The NACC is now the recognized organization for the training and certifying of Catholic chaplains and CPE supervisors.

To understand where CPE is today and to understand the relationship of NACC to ACPE it is important that we review the history of Catholics in chaplaincy during the last quarter century.

Catholic Chaplaincy

Twenty-five years ago there were no standards, no certification procedures for Catholic chaplains. In fact, chaplaincy was often not considered a "good assignment." Too frequently clergy who were not successful elsewhere were assigned to hospital ministry, and even in these cases it was rarely a full-time assignment. Most patients were cared for by the parish priest who routinely dispensed the sacraments when he or the family or the hospital staff deemed it appropriate. Pastoral care was not even a familiar term in the middle of the twentieth century. Medical and nursing staff saw the priest as a social visitor or one who was called in case of emergency. Professionally speaking, Catholic chaplains were not high, if ever, on the organizational chart. True, there were some outstanding priests who gave outstanding care, but they received little training and less recognition.

At the 46th Annual Meeting of bishops in 1964, Bishop Joseph Brunini is quoted to have said to his fellow bishops:

> At this moment, we are in a most critical position, not only in relation to state mental hospitals, but also in relation to community general hospitals. Since 1957, medical societies, federal and state governments and community organizations attest to the value of the chaplain-patient relationship. It has

been stressed time and time again that the patient in the hospital benefits more from the chaplain who has had special training than from one who has not. . . . The comparison of coverage (between Protestant and Catholic chaplains) by medical staff and patients has been brought to our attention in such a way that puts the Church in a very poor light. . . .[1]

The need was clear. Individual clergymen felt the need for further training, but isolated lectures and peer support were about all they had available.

At the same time some changes took place on the medical scene. A holistic approach to patient care became more popular and successful. Physicians were heard to say to clergy, "She needs you more than she needs me." Attitudes among staff were changing. As their work became more complex and paper-oriented, nurses in particular saw the need for a different kind of caring and listening from the chaplain. Denominational differences were not the problem. Staff looked more toward the professional credentials and the relational interaction with patients than they did at the appointment from the chaplain's own faith body.

Clearly, seminary training followed by ordination was not adequate for the chaplain's task. Increasingly the clergy saw that the sacraments, while essentially important, were not all that patients needed nor were the sacraments all that the chaplain had to offer. Often watching the effectiveness of their Protestant counterparts, the priest looked for more opportunities for training within Catholic circles. Also, religious sisters who were in nursing, administration or education began to see that they had much to offer in ministry to patients.

One organization that clearly saw the need for chaplains and specialized training was the Catholic Hospital Association, now the Catholic Health Association based in St. Louis. Formed within its structure was the Conference of Catholic Hospital Chaplains. This conference met in conjunction with the CHA's annual meeting offering primarily information and support. In 1963 this core group of Catholic hospital chaplains wrote their constitutions and published a newsletter, the *Camillian.*

At the same time much ado about something was taking place both at the grass roots mentioned above and at the higher levels of church administration. In 1964 the competent enthusiasm of the Conference of Hospital Chaplains agreed, with the blessing and support of the CHA, to form their own independent organization which would include training and in time possible certification. One immediate step taken by this group was the publication of the *Apostolate to the Sick* in 1967. In the original manual were clearly stated the qualifications and goals of the would-be chaplain. The first job description included the following:

(1) Daily visitation to each patient.
(2) Frequent administration of the sacraments, particularly encouraging the reception of daily communion.
(3) Special daily visits to the critically ill and others in acute need.
(4) Masses for patients on all Sundays and holy days.[2]

This was a beginning. In 1965 an advisory board was formed and had its first official meeting on March 9, 1965. It was this advisory board that made the formal appeal to the National Conference of Catholic Bishops. The minutes of their meeting on April 27, 1965, read as follows:

The General Secretary presented the request of Catholic chaplains in general hospitals, mental and other health institutions to form a national association of all priests engaged in the chaplaincy apostolate. Such an association would permit the chaplains to keep themselves better informed on the apostolate of the sick, give them better professional status in the hospital field, and inform them fully about such matters as standards, criteria and goals for chaplains. . . . The Bureau of Health and Hospitals fully endorses the establishment of such an association and is willing to help in the formation of the association, and will accept responsibility for it once it comes into being.

Cardinal Ritter (Archbishop of St. Louis) moved: that the Administrative Board give its approval and encouragement to the Catholic chaplains serving in hospitals to form a National Association of Catholic Chaplains to include all priests engaged in the chaplaincy apostolate. Seconded by Archbishop Binz (of Minneapolis), the motion carried.[3]

Such was the beginning of the National Association of Catholic Chaplains. The following year much organizational and financial detailing took place.

As we review the history of Catholic chaplaincy in the United States, training and certification have consistently been an area of concern. The rationale for the need of certification of Catholics stems from the fact that each mainline religious body has the right and obligation to judge the personal and professional readiness of those members who apply for specialized ministry. Thus, endorsement and certification by the Catholic community is both professional and acceptable and well in line with other religious denominations. An option the Catholic clergy had up to this point was to take training sponsored by the Association for Clinical Pastoral Education (ACPE). This association, the history of which has been adequately described above, had as its function the training of chaplains. It was understood that the respective religious denominations would endorse/certify their own clergy who would be functioning in specialized ministries. The only certification that ACPE offered was that of CPE supervisors. In other words, ACPE was and continues to be an educational organization that certifies only educators. Endorsement for certification is required from the respective denominational superiors.

Why did the Catholic group begin a training program when ACPE was well known and had a history of good chaplaincy education? Rev. Michael Mack in his 1980 correspondence to Catholic ACPE supervisors felt that development of CPE in Catholic circles resulted from several factors going back to the 1960s.

> First, some Roman Catholics who had experienced ACPE felt their experiences were too clinical to the neglect of the pastoral. While aspects of that analysis may be an over-reaction, I tend to believe (via our oral tradition in ACPE) that in some ACPE centers and with some ACPE supervisors, the clinical was the predominate to the neglect of the pastoral and theological aspects in the past. I believe our ACPE certification and accrediting processes have brought about a clearer balance, and I have experienced this personally in my twelve years of ACPE. Thus, the development of USCC/CPE may have been in reaction to the developmental phase in the history of ACPE. Another probability (but even harder to be concrete about) is that in the 1960's, as some Roman Catholic priests and religious got more in touch with themselves via the ACPE process (and as Vatican II approached and impacted us), some of these persons chose to leave priesthood/religious life. Some bishops/religious su-

periors felt someone/something had to be blamed (and quite possibly ACPE was named). This later point is conjecture on my part, but, I think, plausible. If these two points are valid, I surmise USCC–CPE emerged largely as a reaction. But then the CPE tradition leading to ACPE also began in reaction: reaction to the state of theological education in the early half of this century.[4]

In time, NACC with its new-found support and enthusiasm initiated training institutes which basically were two-week courses consisting mainly of lectures. Topics included were: relationship of chaplain to the hospital, the relation of chaplain to the medical and nursing personnel, sacraments and liturgy within the hospital setting, ecumenism, medical-moral issues, ministry to psychiatric patients, to the handicapped, etc. However, from the earliest days the NACC leaders knew that training must be expanded. They saw clearly that those ministering in specialized areas needed specialized training. They realized also that church law needed to be pastorally interpreted and applied. These same leaders were concerned that the initial training was almost entirely didactic. It was some time, however, before the training of chaplains took on a wholistic focus. When it did, the leaders of NACC looked more closely at ACPE and its method of training. In its beginnings the NACC did not adopt the ACPE program. In retrospect it seems unfortunate that the early Catholic CPE programs, though using much of the vocabulary borrowed from ACPE, failed to utilize the highly trained skilled supervisors, and therefore diluted the training process. CPE then became confusing, as it was a type of education that differed in its intensity and quality as used by both organizations. At the same time the Catholic men and women who had opted for ACPE training during the years that the NACC was forming held ACPE in high regard. These people reported that growth came through group interaction, increased awareness of self and others, and the learning of personal skills. Students discovered ways to be more at ease with other people and gained in their ability to respond more appropriately when the unexpected occurred. Many students experienced a deepening of their spirituality and a greater awareness of the workings of grace in their lives. The Catholic ACPE supervisors and other trained ACPE persons tended to take an elitist posture and had limited respect for their Catholic trainee counterparts. Again, in the eyes of the writer, this was an understandable posture, but one which did not lead to much mutual acceptance or respect. However, one of the principles that NACC did well to adopt was the insight that the *whole* person needed a kind of formation in order to become the best possible provider of pastoral care. Clearly the type of education that was needed could not happen in the classroom. Process education was called for. Students needed to experience themselves and their world with more flexibility. Personal history, feelings and beliefs needed to be reassessed. This type of process education could not be pre-programed. A change was imperative. Time, funds, availability of competent supervisors and clinical settings became primary questions. These practical issues remain questions today, but programs have multiplied throughout the country. Applicants for hospital ministry training have also multiplied. As lay people became more engaged in direct pastoral ministry, they too sought out clinical training. Also, at this particular period in time it became quite clear that the theological competence that was taken for granted (up to this point all chaplains were priests) had to change with the coming of the Second Vatican Council. Curricula were strengthened in theology and the behavioral sciences. Documented updating of theology and its demonstrated integration became a requirement for certification.

Between 1966 and 1985 progress came fast and sometimes furiously! The NACC grew to be a 3,500 member organization with clear professional standards. In 1985 NACC was authorized by the USCC not only to continue its educational training, but to certify qualified members at the basic, advanced, and supervisory levels.

From 1980 to the present there has been considerable discussion between NACC and ACPE around the issues of training and certification. Increasing similarities exist in the standards and in the programs of training in these two organizations. Both organizations concur in their definition of clinical pastoral education; namely, CPE is education in applied theology which integrates theological knowledge with spirituality and psychology. It brings the seminary student, the lay student, and the experienced clergy person into supervised encounters with spiritually, emotionally, or physically troubled persons. Both organizations agree that each CPE participant is responsible for providing pastoral care to patients, parishioners, family and staff in the hospital or parish where he or she is assigned. Among the common goals in both ACPE and NACC programs are: to gain a deeper understanding of oneself as a person and as pastor, to provide experiences for understanding and empathizing with others, and to offer training in pastoral care that can be applied to all areas of ministry. Hence the personal, pastoral and professional identities are clearly the work of the basic programs in clinical pastoral education.

In addition to the goals, similar curricula include lectures, individual and group supervision, case conferences, theological reflection, interpersonal and verbatim seminars. It is in this context that each participant is expected to demonstrate an openness and willingness to explore his or her personal and pastoral identity, interpersonal relationships, and examine in depth his or her attitudes, values, and assumptions about life, suffering, and death. (See diagram "Learning Through Clinical Pastoral Education.")

It can be readily seen that CPE is one of the more recent, more creative, more process-oriented, action/reflection educational models. Its mission lies in its effort to bring the qualified lay person or the trained minister into supervised encounters with persons in crisis so that troubled persons can experience a minister who is personally able, professionally competent, theologically informed, and reasonably integrated.

The NACC continues to be a professional organization whose first concern is the ongoing educational, theological and pastoral formation of its members. Its secondary purpose is to help its members to be an advocate of ethical, legal, political, and social concerns in the health care field. By study and continuing education the NACC works toward developing in its members an awareness of the political, legal, and social issues affecting pastoral care ministry. The two organizations of ACPE and NACC have an increasing and ongoing appreciation for their respective and unique contributions to chaplaincy. Where feasible and desirable, CPE centers are accredited by both organizations. As history indicates, often when there are parallel developments in growing organizations even more dialogue for mutual understanding and growth is called for. This too has happened in recent history as NACC is well represented in COMISS (the newly formed Congress on Ministry in Specialized Settings). The participation of NACC in Dialogue 88 provided a strong incentive to its members to continue to participate in ecumenical dialogue with other organizations with similar goals and functions. Such a mission requires cooperative participation that can provide a bridge by which relationships can be fostered for the good of the people of God. NACC is quickly moving in such a direction. It has achieved recognition among national associations involved in health care. NACC speaks with confidence, cooperation and professionalism, and while cooperating ecumenically it continues to maintain and strengthen its own identity. It is for these reasons that the National Association of Catholic Chaplains maintains its existence.

History continues in the making!

Notes

1. Marilyn N. Gustin and Rev. Msgr. Harold A. Murray, *The National Association of Catholic Chaplains: A Twenty-Year History (1965–1985)* (Milwaukee: Special Publications, Vol. 1, No. 2, August 1985).

2. Ibid., p. 6.

3. Ibid., p. 7.

4. Rev. Michael Mack, *Reflections: ACPE–NACC–USCC*. Manuscript addressed to Roman Catholic ACPE Supervisors, February 1981. Dubuque, Iowa.

Kevin F. Tripp

Certification of Pastoral Personnel

Introduction

The purpose of this chapter is twofold. First I shall present some background and philosophy of certification. I shall then offer some specific information about the certification of chaplaincy professionals, using the standards and procedures of the National Association of Catholic Chaplains as an example. It is hoped that as a result the reader will have a better idea of what certification is, why it is important for ministry, and how it is achieved by some Catholic pastoral ministers and educators.

For many centuries, persons who function in particular roles have been expected to be "credentialed." The word "credentialed" comes from the Latin "credere," which means "to believe." Thus, the person who was credentialed became more believable. Others could rely on that person to function appropriately in the designated role. A credentialing process serves three groups: the public, the profession and the person credentialed. It serves to protect the public by providing information as to practitioners who have satisfied qualifying criteria, and by discouraging quackery. It serves the profession by restricting and protecting the right to practice, and by controlling the standards of training and of practice—which in turn protects the public. It serves the credentialed person by providing a group identity, a symbol of status achievement, professional orientation, and, usually, a guiding code of ethics which in turn is of value to the public.[1] Credentials have taken on many forms. They include academic degrees, ordination, ecclesiastical endorsement, licensure and certification. The criteria for credentialing a person usually include knowledge of theoretical information pertinent to the function, ability to perform the tasks of the role, and the validation that the individual is able to integrate knowledge and skill in the role. The credential is granted by an individual or representative group relating to the publics which the credentialed person will serve.

147

In more recent years, for various reasons, the credentialing of persons has taken on new importance. With reference to church ministry this is true because there is a new awareness of the need for special education and recognition of ministers who serve in special settings. Also, agencies who employ those ministers, or chaplains, frequently require that they be properly credentialed. For many employers, certification provides a helpful tool in selecting qualified personnel, along with other indicators such as educational background, related job experience, personal and previous employment recommendations, and skill reviews.[2] We are experiencing an expansion in ministry today which includes persons who are not ordained. However, the expectation that persons be properly credentialed arises, not from that expansion, but from the rise of professionalism in the helping professions. Employers in institutions, agencies and other specialized settings expect persons working there to be properly prepared for their work. This results in the chaplain being required to be credentialed.

When referring to the credentialing of church personnel, we may be referring to ecclesial and/or professional credentialing. Ecclesial credentialing would include: commissioning, instituting, ordaining or endorsing. Professional credentialing would include: certifying or licensing. In the Roman Catholic tradition, lay persons may be commissioned or instituted for ministries. They would be commissioned for ministries such as catechist or eucharistic minister.[3] They would be instituted into the ministries of reader and acolyte.[4] Ordination (or its faith group equivalent) is a public conferring of authority upon an individual to engage in specific functions on behalf of a religious body (in Christian terms often defined as "the ministry of word and sacrament").[5] Some faith groups understand endorsement to be a credential. In that understanding, endorsement is a statement that an individual is capable of adequately representing the religious body in a field of specialized ministry outside the parochial structure.

The professional credentials for persons are licensure and certification. In 1971 the U.S. Department of Health, Education and Welfare defined licensure as "the process by which an agency of government grants permission to persons to engage in a given profession or occupation by certifying that those licensed have obtained a minimal degree of competency to insure that the public health, safety and welfare will be reasonably protected."[6] The word "certification" comes from two Latin words, "certus," which means "certain," and "facere," which means "to make"; thus certification means "to make certain." Certification is a process "by which non-governmental agencies or associations certify that an individual is a professional who has met certain predetermined standards specified by that profession for special practice." Its purpose is to assure various publics that an individual has mastered a body of knowledge and acquired skills in a particular specialty.[7] Certification is a voluntary regulation by peer colleagues. The principal difference between licensure and certification is the credentialing agency. Licenses are granted by government agencies and therefore have legally enforceable consequences. Certification is granted by a professional agency which may have disciplinary processes, but these processes do not have the binding force of law.

Professional certification rests on the assumptions that those served by members of the profession cannot adequately judge the merits of professional services received at the time those services are being rendered, and that only members of the same profession are qualified to judge whether one of its members possesses the knowledge and skills to practice the profession in a responsible way.[8] The primary purpose of certification is the promotion of competency. Other purposes are: to promote professionalism; to encourage individuals to remain in the profession; to enhance the prestige of the profession; to avoid external governmental regulations; to improve educational programs; to stabilize job security; to be an income producer; to protect clients/employers from incompetent practitioners.[9] Certification also defines the scope of professional practice. In defining the scope, it places expectations on the professional who is certified to practice within that scope. It may also create professional designations and titles.[10]

The principal goal of certification is the recognition and measurement of competencies. Competencies should reflect personal and professional identity and skill regardless of position, title or academic degree. Competencies should be performance oriented rather than academically oriented. Competence should also reflect the identity and skills of experienced practitioners rather than entry-level individuals. Competencies are recognized and measured by: "1) identifying those aptitudes, skills and areas of knowledge which define acceptable levels of competent functioning; 2) stating those aptitudes, skills and knowledge areas in terms of measurable criteria; and 3) devising tests of various kinds which demonstrate whether or not acceptable levels of competence have been achieved by entry level candidates."[11] Competence certainly requires knowledge, but it requires appropriate judgment and skills in integrating and applying that knowledge as well. In addition, competence includes non-cognitive components: attitudes; communication skills; personal attributes such as ethics, values and acceptance of responsibility.[12]

In the pastoral care, counseling and education movement, standards have been developed regarding personal, theological and professional competencies. Competencies are measured in a variety of ways. The National Association of Catholic Chaplains uses a rather traditional process. This process includes the gathering of data (documents, etc.) and writing papers. These materials are presented to a committee which may itself be the certifying body or it may be the delegate of the certifying body. The candidate meets with the committee. During the meeting the committee determines whether the written materials adequately document compliance with standards, and whether the candidate adequately demonstrates ability to function at the level of certification requested. From this process the judgment is made as to whether or not the candidate is competent for certification. C. S. Aist points to the subjectivity of this process.[13] The Association for Clinical Pastoral Education, which certifies clinical pastoral educators, is moving toward objectivity in its measurement of standards by requiring that candidates for certification pass a standardized test.

In this introduction I have discussed the credentialing of persons both ecclesially and professionally for ministry. Persons who minister in specialized settings usually need ecclesial and professional credentials. Such credentials recognize them publicly as competent to serve in that setting. This section has described at some length certification as a professional credential. The meaning, philosophy and generic process of certification have been described. I shall now move on to the organization of the certification process in the Catholic Church in the United States.

The Organization of Certification

Currently, the certification process in most instances is under the control of pastoral care associations. In these associations certification is one of the functions of the peer body. Among those associations are the Association for Clinical Pastoral Education, the American Association of Pastoral Counselors, the Association of Mental Health Clergy and the College of Chaplains of the American Protestant Health Association. Many Catholics have been certified by these non-denominational associations. The process of certification which has been organized by the Catholic Church in the United States since the mid-1960s is somewhat different. In this model, the United States Catholic Conference (USCC), one of the two central organizations of the bishops of the United States, has established a body which is authorized to certify in the name of the USCC. From 1966–1983, this body was known as the Board of Examiners (BOE). During that period, the BOE was actually involved in the process of certification. It reviewed all materials submitted by candidates seeking certification as chaplain or pastoral associate (the title given to certified nonordained persons). No meetings of candidates and the board were required at this level. If the board decided that the written materials demonstrated competency, certification was granted. In 1980, documentation of continuing education hours became a requirement for recertification every six years.

Persons who were candidates for certification as supervisor were required to submit written materials and appear before a committee of the board. From this process the board decided whether the candidate was competent to be certified first as acting supervisor and later as supervisor. The term for certification as supervisor was six years. Recertification was then required.

During most of this period, 1966–1983, the Board of Examiners and the chaplains' professional organization, the National Association of Catholic Chaplains (NACC) were both closely associated with the USCC. Members of the board were appointed by the president of the USCC. The NACC, on the other hand, was the voluntary, professional membership organization for chaplains, pastoral associates and supervisors. Both groups were managed by an office in USCC headquarters in Washington, D.C.

In 1980 the decision was made that NACC would change its relationship with the USCC. No longer would it be dependent on USCC for funds, office space and management. The association moved its headquarters to Milwaukee. However, the certification process was retained as described above by the Board of Examiners. Soon, concern was expressed by NACC that the standards and process of certification be revised and upgraded. There was also a desire on the part of many of the NACC membership that more responsibility for the certification process be given to the association. This was a rather tumultuous period in the history of certification in the U.S. Catholic Church.

In 1982 the president of the NACC appointed a Standards Committee. That committee was charged with developing quality standards and processes for certification. (They were also charged

with developing standards for accreditation, but that is the subject of
another chapter.) Some members of the committee had experience
with the standards for certification in other pastoral care organizations. In 1983, the Administrative Board of the USCC reorganized
the Board of Examiners. The new body is the Commission on Certification and Accreditation (CCA). Catholic pastoral care, counseling
and education associations are currently members of the CCA. These
member organizations nominate individuals to serve as commis-
sioners. The commission itself nominates public members. Commis-
sioners are appointed by the president of the USCC. As was the BOE,
the CCA is authorized to certify persons and accredit pastoral education programs in the name of the USCC. However, the certification
process used by the commission is quite different from that used by
the BOE. In response to the urgent request which the NACC made,
that it be more involved and responsible for the certification of its
members, the CCA adopted a new policy. Member organizations
which demonstrate competency in developing their own standards
and processes for certification may be delegated authority to certify
in the name of the USCC by the CCA. The CCA reviews and ap-
proves standards and process for a three-year period. At the end of
the three years, the commission reviews standards and process again.
It may make recommendations and continue or withdraw delegation
to certify. In 1985 the CCA approved the NACC Standards and
Procedures for Certification. In that same year, the general secretary
of the USCC granted NACC the authority to carry out the certification process in the name of the USCC.

In 1983 the president of the NACC appointed a Certification
Commission.[15] (The Standards Committee had become a Standing
Committee of the Association.) Nine persons serve on the Certification Commission for three year terms. Ultimate authority for certification in NACC now lies with the Certification Commission. Appeals
of commission decisions are processed through an Appeals Panel
which is a separate group from the Certification Commission. In
order to assist with the certification process, the commission appoints
a Certification Committee in each of the regions of the NACC. These
Committees have limited authority to make decisions regarding certification. When persons are seeking initial certification as chaplain
or chaplain advanced, the Regional Certification Committees make
recommendations about candidates to the NACC Certification Commission. (More about specifics of the process is discussed below.)
However, when a person applies for recertification as chaplain or
chaplain advanced, the Regional Committee attests to the documen-

tation, grants or denies the request for recertification, and notifies the commission of its action. When a certified chaplain advanced is seeking admission to the supervisory certification process, the person must first consult with the Regional Certification Committee. Without an affirmative report about that consultation, the candidate may not enter the process.

When necessary, Regional Certification Committees may appoint interview teams for the purpose of meeting candidates. These teams make recommendations about the competency of the candidate to the Regional Certification Committee. The committee accepts, denies or amends the recommendation and submits it to the Certification Commission for final action.

Categories of Certification

When a professional association undertakes the function of certification, one of the decisions it must make is which categories of competency it will certify. A related decision is the determination of levels of certification within the categories. From the early days of the organization, members of the NACC have been certified in two categories. One category is that of pastoral practitioner (chaplain and chaplain advanced). The other category is pastoral educator (associate supervisor and supervisor).

Although the criteria necessary for applying for certification are specifically different for each category, general criteria apply for all. In some faith groups ordination is a requirement for certification. In the Catholic Church, any Catholic who meets the application criteria, regardless of ordination, is eligible to enter the certification process. At the present time less than one fourth of the certified members of the NACC are priests; the rest are vowed religious, permanent deacons and other lay persons.

Standards by which individuals become certified vary considerably among professions, but the more common ones include membership in the professional association, successful completion of an accredited program of education and satisfactory performance in written or performance examinations. Achieving certification means public recognition of the individual as being competent at a prescribed level of professional performance.[16] Application criteria common to each category and all levels of certification by NACC are: full membership in the association; pastoral experience; ecclesiastical endorsement;[17] successful completion of a stated number of units of clinical pastoral education at the appropriate level; payment of a fee; preparation of and collection of papers (e.g. CPE evaluations, competency papers, work samples, etc.).

Pastoral practitioners are certified as chaplains or chaplains advanced. Certification as chaplain attests that the person is competent in fundamental areas such as personal and professional identity.[18] Chaplains advanced are chaplains who have demonstrated competence in an area of pastoral specialization,[19] have demonstrated an ability to function with some autonomy, and are able to provide some leadership in ministry (such as administration, etc.).

Clinical pastoral educators are certified as associate supervisor or supervisor. The associate supervisor is certified as such with the expectation that the individual will function with some independence before proceeding to be certified as supervisor. The associate supervisor is certified for two years. That person is expected to be certified as supervisor by the end of that period unless an extension is granted.

Before discussing the process of certification, I would like to say a word about recertification. Recertification is a complex and controversial issue. Three groups are concerned about professional recertification. These are the users of the profession's services, or the public; the profession; and the certified person. The public is concerned that the professional keep abreast of developments in the profession and that the person remain competent. For members of the public, recertification assures this. For the profession, recertification serves as a stimulus to maintain competence by retaining and developing knowledge and skills. The individual professional may welcome recertification as an opportunity to examine and reassure competency, as an opportunity to grow, as an opportunity for peer review and support. However, the professional may also view recertification as a threatening imposition. The overall objective of recertification is to provide assurance that certified professionals are maintaining a given level of competence.[20] The NACC is providing leadership in the pastoral care, counseling and education movement with its requirement of recertification. Some other professional associations have minimum standards and requirements. Others are now in the discussion stages.

All persons are now certified for five years. In 1984, the NACC adopted standards for recertification. Also in 1984 the Certification Commission established a process for recertification.

The Certification Process

For each category and level of certification, the process includes seven steps. For chaplain, chaplain advanced and associate supervisor:

1. The candidate writes to the national office of the NACC requesting materials for a particular category and level of certification.

2. The NACC office verifies the candidate's membership status. The appropriate packet of materials (including the name of the chair of the Regional Certification Committee) is then sent to the candidate.

3. The candidate then submits the application and fee to the chair of the Regional Certification Committee. The chair convenes an interview team, naming the chair, presenter and reader on the team. Date, time and location of the interview are also established at this time. This information is then sent to the candidate.

4. The candidate collects and prepares the required documentation and written materials. They are sent to each member of the interview team at least one month before the interview.

5. The candidate meets with the interview team.

6. If the persons serving on the interview team are not members of the Certification Committee, a report of the interview and recommendations regarding certification (with vote recorded) is submitted to the Certification Committee. If the committee itself interviews, it prepares the same kind of report. This report is discussed. The recommendation regarding certification is affirmed, denied or amended. The Certification Committee's positive recommendations are then submitted to the Certification Commission. Negative recommendations are not submitted to the commission.

7. The Certification Commission discusses and acts on the recommendation of the Regional Certification Committee. The commission may accept, reject or amend the recommendation. The decision is then communicated to the candidate, the Regional Certification Committee and the national office of the NACC.

Persons seeking certification as supervisor follow essentially the same process. The major difference is that the candidate meets a team of the Certification Commission for the interview. This team then makes its recommendation to the full commission. Thus, in contrast to the other categories and levels which are processed at the regional level, certification as supervisor is processed at the national level.

The process of recertification is a peer review. Chaplains and chaplains advanced document their continuing education hours and calculate the hours in specified categories. They then discuss this with another certified member of the NACC who serves as a peer. This peer may make comments and recommendations. The peer reviewer then signs the document. The candidate submits the material to the Regional Certification Committee which reviews and validates the document. This validation recertifies the person.

The process of recertification of supervisors is more extensive. As well as the documentation of continuing education hours required by practitioners, supervisors must also prepare a competency paper and work sample (preferably a videotape of a supervisory session). The supervisor must then meet a team of three supervisors appointed by the chair of the Certification Commission. The team recommends action regarding recertification to the commission which takes final action. The commission may accept, reject or amend recommendations regarding recertification.

Conclusion

In his first letter to Timothy, Paul urges him to "seek after integrity, piety, faith, love, steadfastness and a gentle spirit" (1 Tim 5:11). This is no doubt a goal of every chaplain and supervisor. Certification recognizes this effort in the individual, esteems it as a goal for the profession, and affirms that all who are served by chaplains and supervisors may expect to see these as characteristics of them.

Notes

1. Schofield, 37.
2. Egleston, 48.
3. According to press reports at this writing, it appears that, if some of the recommendations of the bishops at the Synod on the Laity in October 1987 are accepted by Pope John Paul II, the practice of commissioning lay persons for ministry could be expanded.

4. The ministries of reader and acolyte were established by Pope Paul VI in the apostolic letter *Ministeria Quaedam* of August 15, 1972. They replace the minor orders which were suppressed. Lay persons may be instituted into these ministries. However, it is the usual custom to institute candidates for ordination as deacon and priest only. The reason for the custom is that only men may be instituted.

5. Aist, 103.

6. U.S. Department of Health, Education and Welfare, 1971, 7.

7. Styles, 678.

8. Bratton, 23.

9. Gilley, 60.

10. Grad, 8.

11. Aist, 102.

12. Bratton, 24.

13. Aist, 104.

14. Aist notes this as an issue with which other pastoral care organizations need to grapple (p. 105).

15. A note on the concept of commission should be made here. It will help in understanding the relationship of the CCA to the USCC, and the Certification Commission to the NACC. A commission is established by an organization with authority to act for the organization. This means that, while the commission is related to the organization, it has certain autonomy in making decisions. In contrast, a committee is a group established by an organization to deal with certain issues. The authority to decide the issues rests with the organization. Thus, while the CCA is certainly related to the USCC, as the Certification Commission is to the NACC, these groups are authorized to make decisions apart from other organizational processes.

16. Bratton, 23.

17. For Catholics, ecclesiastical endorsement is a written statement by a diocesan bishop or major religious superior that the individual is a Catholic in good standing.

18. For a more extensive description of competencies required for certification, consult the appropriate section of NACC Standards for Certification.

19. Specialties certified by the NACC are: General Health Care, Mental Health, Rehabilitation, Geriatrics and Parish Health Care.

20. Penna, 51.

Bibliography

Aist, C.S., "Professional Certification in the Clinical Pastoral Field," *Journal of Supervision and Training in Ministry.* 3 (1980) 101–105.

Bratton, B., Hildebrand, M., "Plain Talk About Professional Certification," *Instructional Innovator.* 25 (12/1980) 22–24 and 49.

Egleston, M., "Certification: Its Effect on Role Definition and Professional Identification," *Proceedings of a National Conference for Evaluating Competence in the Health Professions.* New York: Professional Examination Service, 1976, 48. (Hereafter cited as *Proceedings.*)

Fickeissen, J.L., "Getting Certified," *American Journal of Nursing.* March 1985, 265–269.

Gilley, J.W., Galbraith, M.W., "Examining Professional Certification," *Training and Development Journal.* 40 (6/1986) 60–61.

Grad, F., "Regulation Through Licensure: Problems and Prospects," *Proceedings,* 8–10.

Gustin, M., Murray, H., *The National Association of Catholic Chaplains: A Twenty Year History (1965–1985).* Milwaukee: National Association of Catholic Chaplains, 1985.

National Association of Catholic Chaplains. *Standards and Procedures for Certification.* Milwaukee, 1987.

Penna, R., "Recertification," *Proceedings,* 50–51.

Pope Paul VI, "Apostolic Letter, Issued *Moto Proprio* by which the Discipline of First Tonsure, Minor Orders and Subdiaconate in the Latin Church Is Reformed," *The Rites of the Catholic Church.* New York, Pueblo, 1976, 726–731.

Pottinger, P.S., Klemp, G.O., *Concepts and Issues Related to Identification, Measurement and Validation of Competence.* Boston: McBer & Co., 1976.

Schofield, W., "Social Issues in Credentialing Health Workers," *Proceedings,* 37–38.

Styles, M.M. et al., "Credentialing in Nursing: A New Approach," *American Journal of Nursing.* April 1979, 674–683.

Summers, T., "Pastoral Certification from a Developmental Perspective," *Journal of Supervision and Training in Ministry.* 3 (1980) 73–85.

U.S. Department of Health, Education and Welfare. *Report on Licensure and Related Personnel Credentialing, June, 1971.* Washington, D.C.: U.S. Government Printing Office, 1972.

Helen Hayes, O.S.F.

Emerging Accreditation Issues

The process of accreditation has been evolving over the past hundred years as professionals have struggled to identify excellence in their varying fields. Accreditation is more than licensure which is regulatory, governmental and based on minimal requirements. Accreditation is evaluative based on standards developed by leaders in the profession involved. In addition to evaluation, elements of consultation and education are found throughout the accreditation process.

In the late 1800s, the need for accreditation became evident. Initially the field of education was the focus in an effort to strengthen and somewhat standardize the proliferating educational programs in a rapidly changing society. The year 1885 saw the beginning of a voluntary accreditation program which has grown to the complex process which serves education today at all levels. Now, in the process of selecting a school, college, university or special program (for example, clinical pastoral education), the applicant routinely seeks information about the school's accreditation status. Credits from non-accredited schools/programs are not accepted for transfer, licensure, and/or certification.

Following the rapid growth in medical science during the last half of the nineteenth century, health care practitioners recognized the need to establish quality measures for health care delivery. The development in 1918 of a national hospital standardization program by the American College of Surgeons was a response to this concern. The first set of standards that were written by members of this professional group was only one page long. Utilizing these standards, members of the college visited all hospitals with over one hundred beds. To their horror, of the nearly seven hundred hospitals visited only eighty-nine met the minimum standards. Of great concern was that many of the well-known institutions of high repute did not meet the standards. Though the statistics were published, the names of the approved hospitals were not. In fact, they were burned! These findings so shocked physicians, administrators and trustees that support was readily achieved for a hospital standardization program. When the professional groups involved could no longer handle the expense and the volume of work involved in a hospital accreditation program, the need for a new group was identified. The Joint Commission on Accreditation of Hospitals was organized and became incorporated in 1951.

Though the programs mentioned above are voluntary, they have become widespread and have had a positive impact on the delivery of health care and related human services.

Both education and health care have sought to develop standards which are measurable and whose application ensures an acceptable level of professional service. The development of standards is a never-ending process which is an ongoing responsibility of the professions.

The profession of chaplaincy has its own history of accountability. The development of education of chaplains and chaplain educators (supervisors) is treated elsewhere in this book under the title "Clinical Pastoral Education."

The search for standards which would unify the field of clinical pastoral education began in October 1951 at the Second National Conference on Clinical Pastoral Training and culminated in the adoption of national standards in October 1953 at the Fourth National Conference on Clinical Pastoral Education. The first meeting of the constituting agencies of the Association of Clinical Pastoral Education did not occur until 1967. At this time the four organizations involved in the above conferences began shifting from competition to cooperation to form one association concerned with clinical pastoral education to be known as the Association for Clinical Pastoral Education, Inc. (ACPE). In the ACPE the early focus of the Accreditation Commission was on the supervisor as well as on the program being presented. In essence, the supervisor and the program were reviewed simultaneously. About 1970, a certification committee was established as a subcommittee of the ACPE Accreditation Commission. By the mid-1970s, there were two separate commissions in ACPE—one for the accreditation of programs and one for the certification of supervisors.

The history of credentialing by the National Association of Catholic Chaplains (NACC) also reflects the history and development of this association. At its founding in April 1965 one of the five stated purposes of the new association was:

To encourage and promote the education and training of priests as chaplains through national, regional, and local meetings, and through training programs.

In the NACC's beginnings, the needs for information were so great that initial training was almost entirely didactic. When the need for training of the chaplain as a whole person came into clearer focus, NACC leaders began to look more closely at the Association for Clinical Pastoral Education. Catholic chaplains who had taken ACPE training held it in high regard. For the NACC a most important aspect of training has been the theological and spiritual aspects of personal and professional development.

The early 1970s saw the inclusion of religious and laity in pastoral care ministry, and the need for training increased. In the mid-1970s more effort was given to integrating theology into CPE. Gradually the awareness of the group emphasis of CPE and theological growth was deepened.

As both awareness of the value of CPE and the need for training grew, the need for standards was clear. Programs proliferated. Certification standards were continually being upgraded and by 1974 the need to develop standards for the accreditation of training programs was addressed. The years from 1976 to 1980 brought further development of the standards for both certification and accreditation. At this time credentialing processes were conducted by the Board of Examiners of the United States Catholic Conference.

From 1980 to 1984 the question of who should certify and accredit was paramount. As the NACC developed as a professional association, there was an increasing desire to develop and implement its own standards and processes for certification and accreditation. After much intense dialogue and negotiation between the NACC, the Board of Examiners and the United States Catholic Conference representatives, a new body was formed, called the United States Catholic Conference Commission on Certification and Accreditation. New standards were written by the NACC and adopted in 1983.

In both the NACC and ACPE processes there has been a gradual growth to well-defined standards, careful and extensive self-studies and site visits which serve both to validate the self-study and provide consultation and education as part of the process. Within recent years there has also developed a candidacy review with a feasibility study and an on-site visit. The candidacy visit has as its purpose to answer the question: Is it feasible for this institution to consider developing a clinical pastoral education program? Following a period of candidacy (a period of one to four years) a center may then apply for accreditation.

With increasing collaboration between the ACPE and the NACC there has been a growing number of centers that wish to be accredited by both associations. This follows upon a significant number of supervisors who are certified by both the NACC and the ACPE. From growth in dual accreditation has come a movement toward joint accreditation. For a long time, that seemed to be "a dream for the future." Today, with the growing collaboration between the two associations and with the developing trust and mutuality that characterize relationships, we are closer to making the dreams become a reality. Not only is the climate ready, but there exists an organizational structure which could support this new endeavor—namely, the Congress of Ministry in Specialized Settings (COMISS).

Throughout the 1960s and 1970s representatives of professional pastoral organizations met yearly in an Interorganizational Consultation sharing concerns and exploring standards for their accreditation and certification processes. In the 1970s, faith group representatives, including Catholic, Jewish and a wide range of Protestants, successfully formed separate councils through which to relate to two groups—the military/VA chaplains and the federal prison chaplains. With this model of successful interfaith cooperation, it was suggested that a council to handle the concerns of clergy in specialized settings be formed. The council was formed, adding to the faith representatives a voting member of each of the professional chaplaincy and clinical pastoral education organizations. The result was the approval in April 1979 of the organization of the Council on Ministries in Specialized Settings. Within two years it became apparent that the pastoral care organizations had issues to work out among themselves. In May 1981 a meeting of representatives of the pastoral care organizations resulted in the formation of a group to be known as Joint Issues in Pastoral Care Organizations (JIPCO) which would function under the aegis of the parent organization, COMISS. With yearly meetings of COMISS and twice yearly meetings of JIPCO the structures were in place for growing collaboration and the emergence of a unified voice for chaplaincy.

For over twelve years pastoral care organizations in the United States tried to get the Joint Commission on the Accreditation of Hospitals (JCAH) to include pastoral services as a department to be reviewed in health care settings. However, the JCAH remained firm in not adding to its already extensive responsibilities. The attitude prevailed that if it is chaplaincy, "it must be good." Unfortunately, experience has shown that is not always true. In a paper presented by Kermit Smith of the College of Chaplains in November 1983, he speaks of the "unchanged attitude" of the Joint Commission on Accreditation of Hospitals regarding chaplaincy being included as a recognized service or department in a hospital.

As a result of this negative stance by the JCAH, pastoral care organizations began to look seriously at developing a Joint Commission on Accrediting Pastoral Services with standards and a commission that would accredit pastoral care services/departments. Within this vision was a plan to relate in some way to the existing accreditation of training centers that already existed within ACPE and NACC. Pastoral counseling centers were included in the vision.

As a result of these continuing deliberations, the December 1983 minutes of COMISS reflect the approval of the Guidelines for Evaluation of Pastoral Care Departments and the delegation to JIPCO of the task of further exploration of the process of developing standards for the evaluation and accreditation of pastoral services in various settings. At the June 1984 meeting of JIPCO it was moved that the COMISS Guidelines for Evaluating Pastoral Services be taken back to the pastoral care organizations and their response brought back to the December 1984 JIPCO meeting. At this June 1984 meeting of JIPCO it was also agreed to form a task force of organizational representatives to explore future directions toward evaluation and/or accreditation of departments.

The response of the pastoral care groups, made at the December 1984 JIPCO meeting, indicated that the Guidelines for Evaluating Pastoral Services provided an excellent basis for reviewing the quality of pastoral services being conducted in specialized settings. It became apparent during this meeting that institutional chaplaincies felt considerable urgency to initiate a joint accreditation effort whereas pastoral counseling agencies felt somewhat less urgency. It is important to realize that at this time the pastoral counseling association was the only group to have a functioning accreditation process for service agencies. It was agreed by consensus to pursue the special consultation with representatives of pastoral care to plan toward implementation of a joint accreditation process.

The joint accreditation consultation was held just prior to the June 1985 JIPCO meeting. After considerable dialogue to define what exactly was meant by joint accreditation a consensus was reached to recommend to JIPCO the formation of a Joint Commission on Accreditation of Pastoral Services and Education (JCAPSE).

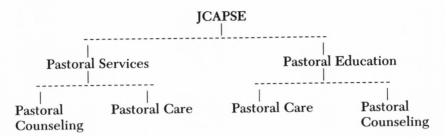

The advantages of joint accreditation are both philosophical and practical. Philosophically, the sharing and dialogue necessary to implement this joint endeavor is a significant move toward unity among pastoral care groups and representatives of a variety of faith traditions. Within this unity is an acknowledgment of diversity which can serve to strengthen unity. Practically, joint accreditation is cost-effective. A center may request to be reviewed for pastoral services and/or pastoral education and under either of these broad headings may request review for pastoral counseling and/or pastoral care. The implementation of this joint program would make possible one study, one site team and one fee.

As has been apparent in the other accreditation programs mentioned earlier, quality control of both education and service is the result of a well-administered accreditation program.

Since there was no accreditation of pastoral services being done by any of the pastoral care associations, it was agreed to begin the joint endeavor at that point. A Standards Task Force was formed to take the Guidelines for Evaluating Pastoral Services and formulate clearly defined measurable standards that would be used in the accreditation process. A Joint Commission for the Accreditation of Pastoral Services (JCAPS) consisting of nine members was established in December 1987. Those who chose to participate in this were the Association of Clinical Pastoral Education, College of Chaplains, National Association of Catholic Chaplains, Association of Mental Health Chaplains, U.S. Bureau of Prisons, two representatives of the religious endorsing bodies and two public members chosen by the commission. With the preliminary work completed, the first site visits were planned for the fall of 1988. We have begun another phase in documenting and defining the profession of pastoral care. New issues have begun to emerge.

Over the past thirty-six years, the voluntary program of accreditation of health care facilities by JCAH has been demonstrated not only as essential to marketing but also as a factor in health care economics. With the proliferation and complexity of payment for health care along with an increasing demand for public accountability for quality, a new challenge is upon us. In order to prepare to meet this challenge, pastoral service needs to "catch up." With increasing pressure for accountability in the use of public money, we need to be able to document through professional standards and review the excellence of the care we provide.

The accreditation process assists in documenting that structures and processes are in place for the delivery of quality care. Accreditation becomes the first step in beginning to look at and assess the outcomes of care. Increasingly, accreditation will be looking to measuring whether we actually do what we show we can do. The theory and practice of methods to measure quality have long been a part of industry. Today, health care, including pastoral care, is having to become serious about the development of quality assurance programs.

The JCAH, newly named JCAHO (Joint Commission on Accreditation of Health Care Organizations), is leading the way in revamping their accreditation process. In a paper written in 1987, the target date for completion of this project is 1991. They state that both clinical and organizational excellence are essential components of quality and that it is timely and appropriate to undertake more direct assessment of both.

In the field of pastoral care, the Catholic Health Association (CHA) has initiated a Quality Assurance Project in twenty-one carefully selected departments of pastoral care. Under the direction of Lawrence Seidl, CHA's Senior Associate, Pastoral Services, the goal for completion of this study was April 1989 in order to allow for the publication of a refined document entitled *Quality Assurance and Pastoral Care* in early 1990.

For pastoral care-givers this is an opportunity to identify more clearly who we are and what we do. As an integral part of the health team in the care of the whole person, we are challenged to become more articulate about our contribution. What do we do that no one else does? How is the healing process facilitated by our unique ministry? How do we document that?

Pastoral care is well on the way to a professional assessment of our programs and services. With the rapidly expanding technology available to us, ongoing evaluation can hopefully become an integral part of our pastoral care practice. As the body of knowledge regarding clinical pastoral care grows and becomes more clearly defined, the relationship of pastoral care to the healing process can be documented. The future of pastoral care ministry rests on our ability to continue our growth in the areas of credentialing and quality assurance.

Barry K. Estadt
in conjunction with
William J. Moorman, O.SS.T.

Pastoral Counseling
in the Health Care Setting

No setting more compellingly forces us to wrestle with the meaning of existence than a hospital room. Whatever the cause of our hospitalization, we are thrust into a situation in which it becomes increasingly difficult to deny our mortality. Hospitalization for an illness, accident or operation, even though not classified as life-threatening, leads us to seek with a heightened awareness the personal meaning of our life journey, asking in a variety of subtle ways the basic questions: Who am I? Why am I? What have I been doing with my life? How much longer do I have? What do I really believe about a life hereafter? When our life is threatened, we face these questions all the more urgently. Sometimes a hospitalization forces us for the first time to grapple with our personal finiteness, our awareness and experience of the holy, our capacity for faith and trust in God and our ability to accept our own personal journey with its richness and its limitations.

Many of us are not used to facing these questions head-on. We keep ourselves occupied with projects, activities and interests which focus our attention and call forth our energies. When faced with hospitalization, the rug of routine activities is pulled out from beneath us. We are removed from the supports that we have carefully built into our personal environment. We lose the sense of "being in control" of our lives. For some it is a time of experiencing an inner alienation that has been successfully repressed through involvement in pursuits and activities which distract from one's inner experiences. It is lonely to face one's innermost core when there is no one with whom to share the intensity, the depth and the content. It is even more lonely when we are unreconciled within ourselves, when we do not know how to reach out to others and when we experience our-

167

selves abandoned by God. The agony of the unreconciled patient can
resemble the agony of Jesus in the garden before he undertook the
final steps of his journey. "Father, let this chalice pass from me."
Jesus endured hours of sweat, struggle and prayer until he arrived
exhausted, but free: "Not my will but thine be done."

So often patients reveal very little to those around them. Sharing
such thoughts and feelings is risky and unfamiliar. Relatives, colleagues, friends and even loved ones are accustomed to our defenses,
and they expect us to keep them up. In their own attempts at denial
they talk of trivia and portray a shallow optimism. Nurses may be
caring and supportive, but their primary focus is task-oriented as
they attempt to meet the increasing needs of patients with fewer
staff. Physicians are skilled diagnosticians in addressing physical
issues but are not usually trained counselors or ministers. The chaplain with training in pastoral counseling has a unique opportunity for
dealing with patients in a holistic way as patients struggle not only
with physical wellness but also with emotional wholeness and spiritual integration. The chaplain with training in pastoral counseling has
a rare opportunity for an in-depth intensified short-term counseling
relationship with results comparable to years of therapy under normal conditions of stress. The hospitalized patient's defenses are
down. A sense of urgency leads the patient to cut through layers of
resistance to get to the core of one's being. Frequently patients find
themselves alienated from themselves, from significant persons in
their lives and from God. The pressure of powerlessness experienced
waiting for a biopsy report can give a patient an entirely different
perspective on life. How many things we would like to have the
opportunity of changing. We promise, we bargain, we beg. We touch
the reality of our aloneness. We experience a frightening and mysterious dependency on the source of life. We yearn for peaceful resolution of old enmities, wanting to sever ourselves from the heavy
bondage of anger, bitterness and hate. We yearn to be free, to be
whole, to be reconciled with ourselves, with others and with God.
The chaplain with pastoral counseling training is in a unique position
to serve as an agent of God's reconciling love.

Pastoral Counseling:
A Contemporary Form of Pastoral Care

In reflecting on and seeking to conceptualize the role of counseling within the chaplaincy ministry, Henri Nouwen's simple

scheme presented in *Creative Ministry* is helpful. Nouwen orders the many activities of ministry under five headings: preaching, teaching, organizing, celebrating and individual pastoral care. In this chapter pastoral counseling will be treated as a specific form of individual pastoral care in which ministers utilize the knowledge and skills derived from the contemporary helping professions within a ministerial and theological framework.

Historically, individual pastoral care has been a rich part of the tradition of Christian ministry. W. Clebsch and C. Jaekle, in *Pastoral Care in Historical Perspective,* describe the functions of individual pastoral care under the headings: healing, sustaining, guiding, and reconciling. *Healing* entails helping a person to be restored to a condition of wholeness; *sustaining* consists of helping a hurting person to endure; *guiding* involves assisting perplexed persons to make confident choices; *reconciling* seeks to reestablish broken relationships with others and with God. The authors relate these four functions to eight periods of church history from, "Primitive Christianity" to the present "Post Christendom Era." While individual pastoral care has been a part of Christian ministry for some twenty centuries, the effort to reach these goals through the process of pastoral counseling is a twentieth century phenomenon.

Pastoral counseling, as a specific form of pastoral care, attempts to combine insights and techniques derived from the contemporary helping professions with the insights of theology, faith and ministry. James W. Ewing (1983) describes the role of pastoral counseling utilizing the metaphor of "bridge." "Because the field links together religion and behavioral science, and consequently sacred tradition and secular lifestyle, it functions as a structural bridge over the chasms of contemporary compartmentalization of knowledge and professional activity. Those persons attracted to the field usually function with multiple intellectual and professional commitments. At a time when our western culture is witness to rapid change and fragmentation, pastoral counseling is attempting to bridge such through attention to the integrative and holistic process of human living and knowing."

The goal of training in pastoral counseling is to provide the minister (ordained, vowed religious, lay) with the opportunity to work toward a synthesis that includes: (1) an incorporation of the body of knowledge common to the field of counseling theory and practice, (2) the development of specific counseling skills, (3) an ability to enter into a deep and trustful relationship quickly, (4) an intuitive understanding of how to facilitate therapeutic progress which addresses simultaneously the whole person: physically, intellectually, emotionally, socially and spiritually, and (5) a clear understanding of one's role as minister.

Profile of a Pastoral Counselor

In the book *Pastoral Counseling* (1983), I wrote a chapter sharing much of my personal and professional journey as a pastoral counselor. I described the pastoral counselor as a *"religiously integrated person . . . who approaches others with a sense of mystery . . . along with an ability to enter into communion with others in a therapeutic alliance . . . with the goal of reconciliation and personal religious integration."* I would like to offer that same schema in this chapter but with entirely new reflections which incorporate my ongoing personal journey. In doing so I am amazed at how none of us can stand still; we either move ahead or fall behind.

A Religiously Integrated Person

I have come to realize over the past few years that "religious integration" is a "theoretical construct." It is a state that we work for but never quite achieve. We reach, with some relief, a level of "functional integration" for a period of time only to find our sought-for integration challenged from within and from without. Our journey is never completed; we go on and on and on! St. Augustine said it so well: "Our hearts are thirsty until they rest in you." It is our commitment to our ongoing personal religious journey which qualifies us personally for ministry. We are not religious gurus but we can be genuine co-pilgrims with those to whom we minister.

When I reflect on the concept of "religious integration," I think in terms of four inter-related elements. These include: (1) *an acceptance of one's finiteness*, (2) *an awareness of the holy*, (3) *a faith which transcends the here and now together with a personal capacity to trust*, and (4) *a grateful acceptance of one's personal pilgrimage*.

Some years ago I wrote about getting in touch with my own *personal finiteness* in dealing with the death of my father in my thirties and my mother in my forties. As I approached, the fifth decade of my life, I got in touch with personal finiteness from within. The sudden and unexpected death of a colleague and friend drove home the reality that the majority of my years were behind me. When I received word of Tom's death by phone, I handled it calmly and went about rearranging a very crowded schedule in order to make attending the funeral possible.

When I first entered the church where his body lay, I paused in a rear pew. I was engulfed by the feeling of not wanting to see Tom in the coffin. I could not believe my reaction. I forced myself down the aisle. On beholding Tom's lifeless body I felt a mortal attack from within. I struggled for breath, my heart pounding. The boundaries of reality and unreality were momentarily blurred. I was in and out of myself, in and out of the coffin. Viewing Tom was viewing myself. Terror turned to grief as the tears streamed. The tears and emotions which surged were complex and came from deep within my being. As I look back on that experience, reliving it with lesser but still powerful intensity, the tears speak to me of the transitoriness of everything and everybody. Tom's death severed a relationship begun at thirteen years of age in a high school preparatory school. The relationship in recent years was becoming closer and richer. It felt incomplete and unfinished. Tom, however, had found completeness through a mysterious journey from life through death to the fullness of life.

During the summer of 1984 I experienced an *awareness of the holy* in three very special places. The first place was Fulda, Germany, where I visited with relatives in the little farm hamlet in which my great-grandfather had been born and raised. Frank left Germany at age sixteen along with others from the Fulda area to come to the new land and to found Fulda, Ohio. It was fascinating to share the hospitality of Frank's brother's descendants so reminiscent of what I had experienced as a youngster in Fulda, Ohio. An unexpected treat, however, was the opportunity of praying in the little chapel and cemetery located on the family estate, both of which dated back to the 1600s. There was a profound sense of continuity with my family roots and with the mysterious workings of providence in the unfolding of my family history. The second special place was the remote changeless medieval village of Assisi, which delights visitors with its thirteenth century charm and intrigues students of Franciscan history. Praying at the tomb of St. Francis was awe-inspiring as I marveled at how this man from a remote village of Italy has so profoundly impacted the world. Again there was a sense of being in touch with the sacred through the spirit of St. Francis. The third special place was Rome. I had the opportunity of participating in a liturgy led by the Holy Father, Pope John Paul II, which included clergy, religious and laity from across the world. There was a profound feeling of unity amid the incredible cultural and political diversity of the group. We shared a connectedness through the Holy Father to Peter to Jesus of Nazareth.

Although the sacredness of suffering can be experienced at home as well as any other place, it struck me particularly when in that same summer of 1984 I was privileged to witness *faith and trust which transcended* the harshness of the human condition. I arrived in Lourdes in the early afternoon which allowed time to visit the shrines and to browse through the shops. I was not impressed. The evening candlelight service, however, was an experience that is indelibly impressed on my memory. The sight of thousands of processing pilgrims carrying candles and singing Ave, Ave, Ave Maria in English, German, French, Italian, Polish, Spanish, Portuguese was part of the backdrop. The focus, however, was the sight of thousands of sick and crippled pilgrims in wheelchairs and hundreds of bedridden pilgrims on mobile stretchers. There was no hysteria but one could sense the impassioned pleas for healing. Individuals suffering from striking limitations imposed by physical handicaps and debilitating illness transcend their individual limits and collectively gather to share their woundedness in a groundswell of confident faith in the reality of God's loving presence. Lord, let this cup pass from me; but not my will but thine be done. Ave, Ave, Ave Maria! I didn't realize that the tear ducts could work without ceasing for two hours. It wasn't the place, remote and lacking in tasteful development; it was God's loving presence in the assembly of the people. Uncured in body, many found spiritual peace in knowing that they had made contact with God in this place, that they had been heard and could now transcend the limitations of this life with renewed trust. For me, it was a transfiguration experience. Like Peter I did not want to leave this holy place.

A *grateful acceptance* of one's own personal pilgrimage is never complete and final. I see life analogous to riding a raft down an uncharted winding mountain stream. We never know what we will face ahead: calm waters, rocks, rapids. We move ahead, confident that God will be with us. I would never have predicted some of the recent surprises I have encountered on my personal life journey. I have found my understanding of the call of Jesus to seek the kingdom of God to take on new meanings as I have entered into new stretches of my personal pilgrimage. I am indeed grateful for all that has been and look forward to many new and creative ways to respond to the uncharted waters which lie ahead, confident that I am blessed by God when I confidently respond with authenticity and generosity.

Approaching Others with a Sense of Mystery

Pastoral counselors and chaplains share a holistic vision, approaching others with a sense of mystery, sensitive to the transcendent strivings of the people to whom we minister. While we are indeed interested in each person's physical well-being, our special training and ministerial focus is on the inner life and spirit of the person as he or she copes with physical ailments. We marvel at God revealing himself anew as we witness the scriptures coming alive as people deal with issues of suffering, death, resurrection and an acceptance of the divine plan. The experience of God working through the pastoral relationship leads us to approach others with a sense of awe, respect and mystery. There is a sense of co-pilgrimage with those to whom we minister. As a co-pilgrim I realize that the individual's journey is unique, involving the interaction of God and the individual human person. In *Pastoral Counseling,* I wrote:

> I understand co-pilgrim to mean that providence, in some way, has allowed our paths to cross at a particular point, perhaps to run parallel for a while; sometimes for a short walk, other times for an extended period. As co-pilgrim I do not relinquish the professionalism which I bring to my counseling relationships; I am very much the co-pilgrim with professional expertise in the field of counseling and psychotherapy.

Entering into Communion with Others in a Therapeutic Relationship

Pastoral counselors have focused their training on developing an ability to enter into communion with others in a therapeutic relationship. The use of the therapeutic or counseling relationship in ministry is the focus of pastoral counseling training. Degree programs offer a strong background in personality theory, developmental psychology, interpersonal relations, marriage and family dynamics, group dynamics, psychopathology, theories of counseling and the like. But the primary focus in pastoral counseling is on the integration of theory and practice in the person of the pastoral counseling practitioner. Pastoral counseling candidates are challenged to work toward a personal synthesis of theological understandings of ministry and contemporary counseling theory and practice. Pastoral counselors seek to understand human behavior and experience as an integration of the physiological, the intellectual, the emotional, the social and the spiritual.

Melvin C. Blanchette, in *Pastoral Counseling* (1983), writes eloquently of the pastoral counseling ministry:

> Pastoral counseling is one form which that ministry of Jesus
> takes in this age; it is a genuine ministry to the members of
> the Christian community. It follows upon the announcement
> that the reign of God will bring freedom to those held cap-
> tive, joy to those in sorrow, sight to those who are blinded. It
> is shaped by counselors who identify their work with the
> work of Jesus, who has called people to himself that their
> sorrows may be comforted and their burdens eased.
>
> For each individual, the sources of captivity, pain, blindness
> and sorrow take a unique concrete form. To these forms of
> evil, sin, or ugliness, the pastoral counseling process holds
> up the values of the Gospel. For it is from the Gospel and the
> life of Jesus that flow the ethical and moral standards which
> are integral for sound decision-making. Where the client
> enters into the process aware of the concrete forms that
> ugliness has taken in his or her life, the process enhances
> vision so that Gospel-related values may be seen as viable
> alternatives in the day-to-day process of living. The pastoral
> counseling process serves to personalize the liberation of
> Jesus through its one-on-one relationship between the coun-
> selor and client. It personalizes the Gospel further by open-
> ing up possibilities for living through the specific applica-
> tion of these integral values.

In the pages to follow, I wish to share an experience of a young
priest in the first months of his hospital chaplaincy after graduating
from a master's program in pastoral counseling. I found the experience moving and I guess I would hope to be so fortunate as to have a
chaplain with the sensitivity of Fr. Bill in my own final days and
hours. Some readers may raise questions about Fr. Bill's own self-
care issues. Some may see him as new and over-involved, needing to
mature in establishing limits in his role as chaplain. You might conjecture that if Bill continues to get this involved with patients, he will
be a candidate for early burn-out. I am sure all of the questions have
some legitimacy, but I still hope that there are chaplains with the
sensitivity of Fr. Bill available when my own loved ones need help. I
suspect Fr. Bill's experience will bring back memories of your own

ministry and will reawaken feelings of gratitude for grace-filled moments in your own life of ministry.

Fr. Bill writes:

The smacking sound of my shoes as they slapped the terrazzo floor of the hospital corridor seemed to be the harshest sound that evening. In many ways that evening was no different than countless other evenings I had spent overnight at the hospital. As a young priest and chaplain, I've always found this work exceptionally stimulating and challenging, but on that particular night I was tired of people, wanted to hear no problems, and just longed to go to my room and sleep. I prayed there would be no emergencies. It was 9:30 P.M. and I had one more person to see before I could retire. His name was John. He was twenty years old and apparently had been admitted with some anemia problem. It did not appear too serious to me, and I remember thinking that this would be a quick, friendly visit to a young man who really didn't need my help. It was odd that he was on the same floor with the leukemia and other cancer patients. The echo of my footsteps suddenly ceased as I entered the carpeted nurses' station.

It was the same stable group of nurses and aides that were stationed here every evening. They were a mixture of young and old who commonly enjoyed joking to alleviate the tension of working with some of the most pain-ridden patients in the hospital. After exchanging a few joking comments with these women, I asked the charge nurse the routine questions about my final patient of the evening. I fully expected her to say, "No problem; he'll be out of here in a couple of days." Instead, she proceeded to tell me about aplastic anemia.

Aplastic anemia is the medical name given to anemia caused by disease of the bone marrow, which produces most of the blood cells. In addition to usual symptoms of anemia, there is frequently bleeding from the nose and mouth and black and blue spots on the skin. This disorder generally produces fatal bleeding or infection, and the chances of survival are about thirty percent.

She went on to say that this particular patient had been fighting this illness for two months prior to admission to our hospital. He had spent that time in an air-flow isolation room out of human contact at another hospital. Bone marrow transplants had failed, and now there was very little hope that he would survive. She paused for a moment, and in a very loving, almost maternal manner whispered, "You've got your work cut out for you; he is going to be a tough one." I thanked her, feeling the weight of my evening meal sour in my stomach, and again turned to hear the empty echoes of my own footsteps in the sterile hallway. I was scared and angry. I had no idea what I would say to this young man, and had wanted to just go to bed. John's room was the last one on the right at the end of the corridor. There was a sterile procedures' cart outside his room. He was in reverse isolation.

I dressed in gown, rubber gloves, and mask, and quietly knocked on the door. I entered, and there was only the soft glow of the bed light and the television tuned to the closed-circuit station of the hospital chapel. It was silent. John lay in bed, while his mother reclined on the cot next to him.

God, how I hated moments like this. I resented being a priest because in my four years since ordination I had come to feel and feel again the overwhelming sense of impotence in these situations. Pious platitudes, cerebral theology, even sacramental ceremonies would offer little comfort to a young man who was dying. Despite years of theology and psychology, I felt powerless standing in the soft light of that room as two people looked at me.

Marilyn, John's mother, appeared beyond-tired, a look only common to those who stand watch over the last days of another's life. She rose slightly, appearing tense due to my presence. John did not move, only blinking his eyes as I introduced myself. My voice broke their private late night conspiracy of silence. I moved closer to John in order to see him more clearly, and allow him to know that my visit was directed to him. He appeared to have strong, sharp facial features, perhaps due more to the sunken wrath of disease rather than nature. He was obviously thin and weak. His neck remained fairly thick which gave the impression of a once active vigorous young man. His face this evening was bathed in sweat as his brown hair clung to his stark white forehead in awkward entanglements. Intravenous bags and plastic tubing seemed to surround him, creating a plastic jungle as it allowed fluids to enter him as the perspiration flowed out of him. But his eyes were his calling card. Despite the cruelty of his diagnosis and the impersonal surroundings, his eyes remained warm, welcoming, and still so full of life. A look only seen in the eyes of a twenty year old who has had his first sip of life, and desires to be inebriated in its beauty.

I made some light conversation in an attempt to become more comfortable with John, and hoped he would feel the same way toward me. There was something intangibly different with John, though, in the way he seemed to listen, to hear every word, devouring them, and searching for something more. On my part my words were so petty, as are most conversations in the beginning, and yet they were still drawn out of me and appreciated by John. At one point I told him teasingly that I hated wearing a mask because it hid so much of my good-looking face. He gave me a half-laugh and told me he would catch me on TV when I said mass so he could see how handsome I was. I remember we both laughed, and then passed into a moment of sacred silence, the holiness of space which is born at the birth of a relationship. I was relaxed and so was he. I had begun to love the individual who lay so ill in the bed before me. It was then that I spoke words I had never said to the myriad of patients I had seen. I told him I would like to become his friend. Smiling, he nodded in agreement. I went on to say that I did not know how much time we would have to talk, but that our one ground rule would be: no bullshit! We would talk about the important things. Again, he smiled with those consuming eyes, eyes that allowed me to know that I was saying what he also felt, eyes that confirmed even that which had not been spoken. John motioned in agreement. There was another rich moment of silence before I spoke and ended our late evening encounter; "I think we're going to become good friends very quickly."

It had been all of twenty minutes, but we were both tired. I said goodbye with a promise to return the next day. John's mother appeared pleased that he had found someone he could talk with.

I closed his door, removed my sterile garb, and again heard the lonely, tired sound of shoes on a hard floor as I moved toward the nurses' station. The charge nurse was there waiting. Our eyes met and I simply said: "This one is going to break our hearts." She nodded silently and I proceeded down the endless corridor toward the security of my own bed.

Over the next couple of days John's physical condition continued to deteriorate. He became increasingly feverish and lethargic. He would always be grateful when I came to his room and wanted nothing more from me but to hold his hand. For my part I became increasingly frustrated, feeling the need to talk with him. He appeared to have no needs at this time except to receive communion and have me present. I became annoyed because I so wanted to establish this friendship I had spoken earlier about to John, for I believed it would be my vehicle to be of assistance through his dying process. What I would come to know is that what I desired, he did also, and that this was taking place, in spite of myself, through the silence we shared.

During these days I grew to know and love John's family for the courage and faith born out of their love for their son and brother. Ray was the oldest child in the family. At twenty-six he had just completed law school and was preparing for his bar exam. I perceived him as understanding his place in the family as one who had to maintain control to help the other family members. He confided to me that his grief was as intense as that of everyone else in his family, yet he felt more free to express this in private. Jenny was the eldest daughter, a beautiful woman who still felt the pains of her own hospitalization a few months earlier from a boating accident. She and her younger sister Joy were transparent with the pain that engulfed them regarding their younger brother's illness. Stuart was eighteen years old and suffered in a most painful way at this time.

Stuart's relationship to John was that of idol, mentor, and god in a baseball uniform. I believe Stuart had only one goal, and that was to become as much like John as possible. To Stuart, John's illness was incomprehensible, and he was consumed with a rage born out of his feelings of powerlessness, and a fear from a dawning sense of vulnerability. The youngest in the family was Jerry, who, like Stuart, stood in awe of John's abilities and winning personality. Jerry was the most alone at this time. He was unable to verbalize the new depths of sorrow and helplessness he was feeling. He would search the faces of his brothers and sisters in the hope of discovering some clue to help him deal with these devastating feelings. Not finding an answer which satisfied him, he often expressed his aloneness in retreating to a corner of the lobby by himself.

John's parents, Raymond and Marilyn, were a couple devoted to each other, and the life meaning derived from living out their vocations as parents. For them the scenario of the hospital was not new. They had lost their first-born child at age seven to viral encephalitis, and knew only too well the horror of pain and death when it grasps one to whom you have given life. Perhaps it is for this reason that the words of the gospel: "Into your hands I commend (his) spirit," most often come to mind when I reflect on the way Marilyn approached John's oncoming death. Her deep faith, a faith interwoven in the very fabric of how she understood herself and God, allowed her to accept John's dying and freely give him back to God. This faith became the naked strength which enabled her to complete her call as the mother of John. When she realized there was nothing more to be done for John, all the needed words spoken, she sat content, holding him and wiping away the clotted blood as it poured from his mouth. At times my faith seemed so inadequate as I watched this woman live her faith each day. Like so many others I have met, she became my teacher at those moments, and yet it was her son who would touch my soul.

John's condition continued to decline as the invading infections became more difficult to combat. Eventually the infused platelets which John had been receiving to control his bleeding were discontinued, and the reverse isolation ended, so that John could approach his death with a greater sense of presence from his family.

Three days before his death I entered John's room at approximately 3:00 A.M. John's father had been keeping vigil, so I told him to take a break while I sat with John for a while. He had maintained a delirious temperature throughout the day, and even then had been semi-comatose. I sat expecting the next half hour to be spent in quiet reflection. Lost in my own thoughts I heard my name whispered. I raised my head to find John, fully awake, staring at me. He then said he needed to talk. I nodded in agreement, and he began to speak of the important things. He spoke of dreams, hopes, goals and family. While he spoke I felt as if, in an inner sense, our focus was narrowing in time suspended moments that only embraced the two of us. Between us there was a distinct ebb and flow much like a warm spring which seemed to cleanse both of us, leaving the exchange vulnerable, yet one of the most natural experiences I have ever felt. All the previous thoughts of myself vanished as I willingly felt consumed by the peace that became so present in the room.

John spoke of his family and what they had meant to him. He spoke about his fears that his younger brothers would grow up making the same mistakes he had made. He spoke of his parents and the guilt he felt for their suffering in relation to his illness, and the pain they would have to live with when he died. In our exchange, I tried to relieve him of these feelings, and believe he found some reconciliation in himself. There were some moments of silence during which what pervaded into my awareness was the knowledge that for me no one else existed at this moment. Some would call this transcendence, but my experiencing allowed me to know in a newly discovered way an uncharted depth of love previously thought incapable for another person I had known for such a little time.

The unbroken silence was ended when John asked me the most difficult question: "Father Bill, what will it be like to die?" I remember looking at him, his eyes now peaceful, serene, not really needing an answer. I responded that I did not know what it would be like for him, but that he would not be alone when it was time to leave us. In this question and answer we confirmed the depth of our feelings in our new-found relationship, and also acknowledged its end. If our relating at this moment had remained in the common sphere of most human relationships, we could have sought redemption in a cathartic cry. But there was something beyond the two of us operative at that moment, something that drew us beyond human emotion. To give it a category in words for understanding, I believe it was a rare grace-filled moment of God's presence, freely sharing his Spirit in the event of John and me. John was answering, for me, too many questions I had not asked about my ability to minister. It became evident that there was someone beyond John, working through John, to answer my own questions of self-doubt.

It was in this brief relationship I found confirmation of my priesthood.

As my awareness of this God-presence in John emerged we continued to speak, and I increasingly felt like the novice entering a secret holy place. I discovered within myself a genuine sense of awe. I felt immersed in the "mysterium, tremendum et fascinans," a description given by the theologian Rudolph Otto of the experience of the Holy. Simultaneously, I became aware that this experience was given birth and nourished out of the loving exchange of two human beings. In those sacred moments I felt unburdened of all cognitive self-will, which had been my primary vehicle of direction and defense, and allowed God to lead me, feeling pliable, terrified, and at peace.

We spoke of heaven, hell and purgatory, but primarily we spoke of God and what he must be like. John even joked that when he found out, he would try to let me know so my job would be easier. What John was unaware of is that he had already let me know. It was time to end our conversation. I do not know why, but we both knew it. John took my hand, and as if he was feeling my recent pains, said: "You are a good priest, Father Bill. I love you." I told him that I loved him, and felt gratefulness and loss together well up inside of me, but turned to leave as words had become inadequate.

During the following two days John's condition deteriorated rapidly. Constantly nauseous, he refused oral medications, and, with the absence of platelets in his blood, began bleeding continually from every orifice. The sustained high fever and loss of blood rendered John disoriented, and his speech inaudible at times. His family waited. Outside his room the nurses began to worry over the never-ending stream of friends which crowded the corridor. Each day his group of friends grew larger, often spending the entire night at the hospital in their silent tribute of love, and their awkward attempt at goodbye. Inside the room his mother continued to wipe away the blood from the face of her son, reminiscent of the beauty of the Pietà. A task born out of the dutiful love of a mother for her child.

It was during these moments of horror and pain, when you think the human body is incapable of enduring this degree of suffering, that quiet miracles are sometimes witnessed. God gave us two. The first occurred when John's fever inexplicably broke for a short time. John sat in bed with his family surrounding him and began to speak of an earlier family vacation taken in Florida. Miracles are ironies that seem to go against nature, yet touch at the heart of life. In the onslaught of their agony, this family laughed, joked and smiled over this special time for them, and for a few brief moments transcended the agony of the present to celebrate the truth of love which spontaneously poured out of each member of the family for the other. This was John's final and greatest gift to his family which I was privileged to witness. In the special moments they shared, John asked them to look beyond the pain of the present and remember the divinely human miracle of the heart, which had bound them together and could not be broken by illness or death.

At 1:00 A.M. I became aware of my own exhaustion and began to leave John's room, saying goodbye to his family. I administered the sacrament of the sick, anointing him with the sign of the cross on his forehead for the final time. I was conscious only of my own weary footsteps as they smacked the floor, and the numbing effect of sleeplessness as it tugged at my brain. Suddenly I became aware of panicked footsteps approaching from behind me. I turned to see John's aunt, wide-eyed, who rapidly commanded; "Come quickly." As I was snatched out of my own haze, she began to explain as we approached the room. Upon my leaving, John had suddenly sat up in bed and began praying the Our Father. As I entered the room it again took on the mystique of a holy shrine where only the uniform chant of the prayer could be heard from every member present. John was strange. Sitting erect, fully conscious, his eyes were transfixed either on the television which had remained tuned to the closed circuit view of the chapel, or focused on the crucifix next to the television. Surprised and uncertain, I too joined this unified recitation, and eventually changed the prayer to the Hail Mary, which beautifully asks the Blessed Mother to pray for us "now and at the hour of our death." Part of the strangeness of this event emerged from the fact that an individual who at best had been only marginally conscious now seemed to lead all of us in prayer. The bleeding had stopped momentarily, but the ravages of illness were still acutely obvious in his face. There was something more in those moments, a new sense of emptiness.

Gone was the presence of John, but there was no lack of presence in the room. In his place was a greater fullness of Presence.

Our praying lasted ten or fifteen minutes at the most, when John again reclined and passed into the inaudible mumblings of semi-consciousness. Doubtless this event would remain unimportant for many and would rarely find documentation in nursing notes. Others could attempt a myriad of undisputable explanations with a valid basis in scientific argumentation. Nevertheless something of significance happened that evening, and most significant events have an underlying reason. I can only offer my subjective interpretation which for me holds much meaning. In those final moments with John, it became peacefully evident that John as everyone had known him was no longer present to us. There were in those moments no feelings of pain, fear, apprehension or remorse in John as those are part of our reality, but rather John was in a state beyond these feelings. John seemed to be in a state of transition from our reality to another reality. The feeling which refuses to leave me, a feeling interwoven with my faith understanding, is that this was a gift of goodbye to his family. A gift which affirmed the faith which we at times tenaciously cling to in life, a faith which at times is confirmed in the dying. Karl Rahner proposes that a state of purgation is not necessarily a state we pass into following death, but rather it is the dying process itself which is purgatorial. Death is the entrance to greater life. If there is truth in this concept for the one experiencing dying, then it is likewise true for the living. It is we who out of faith and love maintain a vigil for the dying. We are also purged indelibly and are given a greater awareness of the mystery of ourselves, others and the presence of God. Perhaps this is what we witnessed in the quiet final miracle of John.

John's physical death occurred a few hours later at 4:10 A.M. His family was present. I was called and again we prayed, before leaving the hospital. As I watched the mechanical movements of family, friends and relatives as they walked away from the front entrance of the hospital, I stood alone and noted to myself the crispness of the early morning air as the sun announced its arrival. It looked as if it was going to be a nice day.

As I drove home that morning I was thankful that I had the day off, and became aware of a river of feelings that flowed through me. Most troubling was the fact that I had not as yet cried over the loss of John. This was strange coming from a person who easily sheds tears over common telephone commercials on TV. I was too numb to really think of anything but sleep, and yet something tugged within me for attention. It started quietly enough as I felt the warmth of tears roll down my face, but as I gave in to my feelings I was soon enveloped by the convulsive grief that had begun to sicken me. Sobbing, shaking, crying John's name out, the feelings of sorrow, helplessness, and love poured out of me, providing the balm for heart, mind, and soul that I had longed for all week. Quietly numb by three o'clock, I could once again love myself and God for the life I was living, the work I was doing, and the feelings that were born of these. Again I heard my footsteps as they climbed the stairs to bed, refreshed in the knowledge that I might cry again, and that it was all right.

It has not been a year yet since John has died. In that time I have struggled for many months against writing the feelings and reflections that surround my experience of John and his death. I have been afraid that I would have to feel my own pain again. As I write this, though, I have a sense of calm about those moments. John touched me deeply, and with a greater depth was my experience of God through John. I have been changed by this encounter, perhaps change measurable only in the new dimensions I experience from my faith. The truth of that faith tells me in an experiential rather than a purely theological cognitive way that human beings are given a multiplicity of possibilities to understand God and our relationship to him in life. Even in the agony of a dying young man like John, or Jesus, God creates in us a faith that states his love for us, for the world, or for even just one young priest.

I have included Fr. Bill's account because it speaks eloquently to me of the sensitivity needed to access the deeper needs of patients if we are to offer them quality pastoral ministry. It also raises issues about pastoral initiative and the type of pastoral presence which invites others to share their story. For me, Fr. Bill's ministry to John beautifully illustrates the description which I offered earlier of the pastoral counselor: "a religiously integrated person who approaches another with a sense of mystery along with an ability to enter into communion with the other in a therapeutic alliance with the goal of reconciliation and personal religious integration."

Pastoral Care Department of the Future

As I look at pastoral care services from the vantage point of being a licensed psychologist, a pastoral counselor and an NACC supervisor, I would suggest that the area of providing "counseling services" is a major growing edge for most pastoral care departments. Traditionally seminaries and theological schools have addressed very effectively three areas of ministry (utilizing the framework of Henri Nouwen referred to earlier), i.e. preaching, teaching and celebrating. Much less attention has been given to Individual pastoral care and counseling. While some priests supplement their ministerial training with counseling courses and even subsequent degree work, the typical seminary does not prepare its candidates for a counseling ministry. Chaplains, especially, need to be prepared to engage effectively in crisis ministry, in supportive short-time counseling, and, in the case of long-term clients, in longer-term therapy. Attention to the patient and to families in coping with catastrophic injury and death is integral to the religious mission of the pastoral care department.

Although all members of the pastoral care department need training in basic listening and responding skills, at least one member of the department should have specialized training, minimally at the master's level, in pastoral counseling so that the department can deal with the patient's emotional and spiritual needs. The chaplain, trained in pastoral counseling, can be of great assistance to physicians, nurses and other hospital staff who invest themselves in serving suffering human beings. The pastoral counselor can play an important role in meeting the deeper needs of patients and in responding to the ongoing needs of family and staff.

Given the declining numbers of priests and religious, it is clear that the future of the pastoral counseling and pastoral care ministry in religious and secular institutions will depend on the openness to lay ministers who have been preparing themselves with formal training in ministry in increasing numbers in the last decade. Many pursue, as adults, degrees in pastoral counseling, pastoral ministry and theology. A large number of graduate programs have developed during the last two decades as alternative ways to prepare for ministry. Many of these programs require an advanced level of maturity and life experience prior to enrollment with a special focus on an integration of theology with personal experience and supervised ministry.

Programs such as the above attract candidates with substantial life experience and a variety of professional backgrounds who seek second careers with a focus on ministry: many vowed religious women who have served in teaching, nursing, and administrative roles and are looking to various forms of individual pastoral care and counseling within parishes and institutional chaplaincy departments; lay nurses, teachers, and social workers who wish to shift from the task-orientation of their professions to a more personalized form of ministry; government and military executives with early retirement who wish to make a contribution to ministry within their churches. In addition, there are many women who during child-bearing years have been active volunteer leaders within their denominations and who have informed their lived faith through the years with regular study groups, workshops, retreats, and courses. New programs which recognize the life experience, mature level of faith, and established professionalism of such candidates have been designed to meet their need for theological and ministerial training as alternatives to the traditional Master of Divinity programs. The theological foundation of the non-ordained ecclesial minister has been addressed repeatedly in the documents of Vatican Council II. The decree *Apostolicam Actuositatem* highlights among other things the active and responsible participation of the laity in the salvific mission of the church as "special and indispensable" to them: "Indeed, the church can never be without the lay apostolate; it is something that derives from the lay person's very vocation as a Christian." The decree *Ad Gentes* underlines the importance and indeed the irreplaceability of the laity in the missionary activity of the church: "The church is not truly established and does not fully live, nor is it a perfect sign of Christ, unless there is a genuine laity existing and working alongside the hierarchy." The constitution *Gaudium et Spes* portrays the involvement of the laity as a significant and decisive moment in the church's relationship to the contemporary world. One commentator has observed: "Lay ministry has been simmering on the 'back burner' of the church for two thousand years. The Second Vatican Council has moved the issue to the 'front burner' and turned the heat up all the way."

Conclusion

The hospital chaplain with training in pastoral counseling may be the only person who can address the inner struggle for meaning and purpose which many patients experience at some level during a hospital stay. So much depends on the chaplain's ability to hear the struggle which frequently is kept hidden just beneath the surface and by the chaplain's readiness and capacity to invite the patient to share that struggle. It requires acceptance, care, understanding, and a capacity to communicate to the patient one's deep concern and availability. It involves a request that the patient lower the drawbridge which guards the castle where one keeps the treasures of one's inner life. As chaplains, we need to assure by our way of being that we will tread lightly. No thought, no emotion, no experience is foreign to us. We share the brokenness of the human condition. We understand woundedness because we have been wounded. We understand hurt and anger because we have been there. We understand anguish and despair because it is not foreign to our experience. We understand sin and repentance because we know our own sinfulness and our personal struggle to accept God's grace. We know the struggle to accept our mortality because we deal with it daily. We know what it is to seek peace within ourselves because we have found it. We know what it means to seek reconciliation from others because we have done so. We know the meaning of accepting our own personal pilgrimage gratefully because we do it daily. We find ourselves able to be ministers of reconciliation because we have been reconciled.

Bibliography

W. Clebsch & C. Jaekle. *Pastoral Care in Historical Perspective.* New York: Prentice-Hall, 1964.

B. Estadt, M. Blanchette, J. Compton. *Pastoral Counseling.* New Jersey: Prentice-Hall, 1983.

H.J. Nouwen. *Creative Ministry.* Garden City, N.Y.: Doubleday, 1971.

Notes on the Contributors

RODGER F. ACCARDI is Vice President-Governance at Wheaton Franciscan Services, Inc., Wheaton, Illinois. He holds a D.Min. from the Chicago Theological Seminary. A certified Supervisor, he is president of the United States Catholic Commission on Certification and Accreditation and is a member of the N.A.C.C. Certification Appeals Panel.

SR. CORRINE BAYLEY is Director of the Center for Bioethics and Vice President of St. Joseph Health System in Orange, California. She holds an M.A. in Religion and Medical Ethics from the Pacific School of Religion and an M.A. in Hospital Administration from St. Louis University. She is publisher of *Ethical Currents* and author of many articles on bioethics.

REV. JAMES BURYSKA is Director of Chaplaincy at St. Marys Hospital of Rochester, Minnesota. A priest of the Diocese of Winona, Fr. Buryska worked in a variety of pastoral settings prior to assuming chaplaincy duties in 1976. He also serves on the Certification Commission of the N.A.C.C.

SR. SARA CARTER is Director of Pastoral Ministry for Santa Rosa Health Care Corporation, San Antonio, Texas and Supervisor of Field Education at the Oblate School of Theology. She is a Sister of Charity of the Incarnate Word and holds an M.T.S. from the Oblate School of Theology and an M.S.N. from Catholic University.

SR. DOROTHY COTTERELL, S.U.S.C. holds an M.Div. from Andover Newton Theological School and is certified as a full Supervisor by both the N.A.C.C. and the A.C.P.E. She is the Associate Director of Pastoral Care and a CPE Supervisor at Interfaith Health Center in Providence, Rhode Island.

BARRY K. ESTADT, Ph.D., is Director of Doctoral Clinical Education in the Department of Pastoral Counseling at Loyola College in Maryland. He holds a Diplomate in Counseling Psychology from the American Board of Professional Psychology and a Diplomate from the American Association of Pastoral Counselors, and is a Certified Supervisor with the N.A.C.C. Dr. Estadt is a licensed psychologist in Maryland, the District of Columbia and Pennsylvania. He is the editor of *Pastoral Counseling* (Prentice-Hall, 1983) and *The Art of Clinical Supervision* (Paulist, 1987).

SR. HELEN HAYES, O.S.F. is Executive Director of the National Association of Catholic Chaplains. She previously served as Coordinator of Education, Certification and Accreditation, and as Associate Director and Acting Executive Director of the N.A.C.C. She is a certified CPE Supervisor and was Director of Chaplaincy at St. Marys Hospital in Rochester, Minnesota before coming to the N.A.C.C. She holds an M.S. in Nursing Education from Catholic University and has authored articles for various nursing journals.

MARGOT HOVER is a CPE Supervisor at Duke University Medical Center, Durham, North Carolina. She formerly was Decedent Care Coordinator at Parkland Memorial Hospital in Dallas, Texas. She holds a D.Min. from the Consortium for Higher Education in Religious Studies. She has worked as Associate Director and Director of Pastoral Care in several hospitals and is the author of a number of books on family life.

REV. ROBERT L. KINAST teaches Pastoral Theology at the Catholic University of America. A priest of the Archdiocese of Atlanta, he holds a Ph.D. in Systematic Theology from Emory University. He is the author of numerous articles and books, the most recent being *Sacramental Pastoral Care* (Pueblo, 1988).

SR. TERESA MALTBY, R.S.M. is Vice-President, Mission Effectiveness for Our Lady of Mercy Hospital, Dyer, Indiana. She holds a D.Min. from the University of Chicago Divinity School and has taught at St. Xavier College, St. Mary-of-the-Woods College and Illinois Benedictine College. She is a regular contributor to *Markings* (St. Thomas More Press).

REV. WILLIAM J. MOORMAN, O.SS.T. is a Doctoral Candidate in the Pastoral Counseling Program at Loyola College, Maryland.

WILLIAM F. NISI is an ordained pastor in the United Church of Christ and a full Supervisor for the A.C.P.E. He holds a Th.M. from Princeton Theological Seminary. He is the Director of Pastoral Care and a CPE Supervisor at Interfaith Medical Center, Providence, Rhode Island.

REV. LUCIEN SAWYER, O.M.I. is Director of Health Care Ministry for the Archdiocese of Boston. He is Past President of the Association of Mental Health Clergy and has served as chaplain at various hospitals in New England. Fr. Sawyer's articles on Pastoral Assessment and Quality Assurance have appeared in the *A.M.H.C. Forum.*

FLORENCE FLYNN SMYTHE has served on the Pastoral Care Staff of Lutheran General Hospital in Park Ridge, Illinois for thirteen years. A registered nurse, Mrs. Smythe has developed programs for training and supervision of lay ministers and seminarians in hospital ministry. She and her husband Walter are the parents of seven children and the grandparents of nine.

REV. KEVIN F. TRIPP is Director of Chaplaincy Services at St. Mary's Hospital and Medical Center in San Francisco. A priest of the Diocese of Fall River, he has been engaged in hospital ministry since 1974. He holds an M.A. in Liturgical Studies from the University of Notre Dame and is a Certified Supervisor for the U.S.C.C. and an Acting Supervisor for the A.C.P.E.

REV. CORNELIUS J. VAN DER POEL is a Counselor and Spiritual Director at Ecclesia Center in Erie, Pennsylvania. He has served as Director of Pastoral Care in several hospitals and was founding Director of the Graduate Program in Pastoral Ministry at Duquesne University. He is a Holy Ghost Father and the author of many articles and books. A certified N.A.C.C. Supervisor, Fr. van der Poel is a former regional director and the editor of the *Special Publications* of the N.A.C.C.

SR. CYRILLA ZAREK, O.P., is Director of Pastoral Care at Maria Health Care Center in Adrian, Michigan. With Rev. Richard A. Tessmer, she coordinates a program, Clinical Experience of Pastoral Education for Parish Coordinators of Ministry of Care to the Sick, at the Center for Development in Ministry, University of St. Mary of the Lake, Mundelein, Illinois. She has co-chaired the Task Force on Pastoral Care for the Archdiocese of Chicago and has served as Adjunct Professor at Catholic Theological Union, Chicago, as Coordinator of Pastoral Education for Mercy Hospital, Chicago, as N.A.C.C. Coordinator of Education, and as a Field Supervisor for C.T.U. She initiated a parish-based C.P.E. program in 1984.

DATE DUE